Global Warming

Global Warming

The Debate

Edited by

Peter Thompson
Strategy Europe Limited

with the assistance of

John P. O'Hara
Denton Hall Burgin and Warrens

Published on behalf of
STRATEGY EUROPE LIMITED
by
John Wiley & Sons
Chichester · New York · Brisbane · Toronto · Singapore

John Wiley & Sons Ltd, Baffins Lane,
Chichester, West Sussex PO19 1UD, England

Other Wiley Editorial Offices

John Wiley & Sons, Inc., 605 Third Avenue,
New York, NY 10158-0012, USA

Jacaranda Wiley Ltd, G.P.O. Box 859, Brisbane,
Queensland 4001, Australia

John Wiley & Sons (Canada) Ltd, 5353 Dundas Road West, Fourth Floor,
Etobicoke, Ontario M9B 6H8, Canada

John Wiley & Sons (SEA) Pte Ltd, 37 Jalan Pemimpin #05-04,
Block B, Union Industrial Building, Singapore 2057

British Library Cataloguing in Publication Data:

A catalogue record for this book is
available from the British Library.

ISBN 0-471-93157-8

Printed in Great Britain by Courier International Ltd, East Kilbride

From: The Rt Hon. Earl of Shannon

House of Lords

1991

There is no doubt that the global warming debate is now in the forefront of public awareness, although related issues are still the centre of much discussion.

The United Nations Conference on Environment and Development (UNCED), taking place in Brazil in 1992, proposes to embrace all possible avenues of global climate issues: poverty, desertification, agriculture and economics, population growth for example.

Here, in London, the international Global Warming Debate at the Royal Society, so excellently conceived by Peter Thompson, Deputy Chairman of Strategy Europe Limited, was a significant event, which I had the privilege to chair.

This high level Debate proved an original opportunity for many of the world's leading experts on economics, business/industry, environmental law, energy and transport to present their opposing views, through the Debate's unique structure: a series of specialist debates during the two days of the event.

Naturally, such an event would have been impossible were it not for the keen interest of speakers, who came from seven different countries. The delegates too, who came from nine different countries, played a very significant part, through their attendance and contribution, throughout the two days.

We were all encouraged by the Minister for the Environment and Countryside, Mr. David Trippier, for attending the Debate, as we are for his kind and perceptive thoughts in the introduction of this report.

This Report has come into being largely thanks to Shell International Limited, to whom we are all very grateful, and to the very valuable contribution of John P. O'Hara, of Denton Hall.

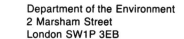
Department of the Environment
2 Marsham Street
London SW1P 3EB

*Minister for the Environment
and Countryside*

Telephone 071-276 3440

DAVID A TRIPPIER RD JP MP

Global warming and consequent climate change are amongst the key environmental issues facing the world today. The Government is committed to respond to this threat, through internationally agreed action and by taking action at home to reduce Britain's emissions of green house gases.

This action will involve everyone from policy makers to businesses, householders and consumers. We are all, in one way or another, responsible for emissions of greenhouse gases, because we all use energy for heating and lighting our homes and offices and in transport, as well as in industrial processes.

It is essential that all sections of society are aware of the risks of climate change, its causes and what can be done about it. I was therefore very glad to attend the wide-ranging and timely debate organised by Strategy Europe on this issue. The publication of this report will I hope help to spread understanding further.

100%
RECYCLED PAPER

GLOBAL WARMING:
THE DEBATE
7th & 8th March 1991

1991

Peter Thompson
Conference Director

In April 1990, Strategy Europe Limited had taken a hard look at the Environment Protection Bill, for it did not appear to have a national waste policy or strategy.

In an endeavour to prompt the Government, of the day, to concede the necessity for a waste policy and strategy, I took it upon myself, with The Earl of Shannon, to conceive and set up an international debate on the theme of "A Call for a National Environmental Waste Policy".

The conference took place at the House of Lords and, shortly after, the Government admitted that, while it had a regional strategy on waste, it did not have a national policy. It could be argued that this is no longer the case.

Following on from the House of Lords conference, it was suggested to Strategy Europe by a nationalised industry in June 1990 when there was no gulf conflict or pressing recession, that an international debate on global warming should take place, in the public's interest. This it did and, thanks to Shell International Limited and John Wiley & Sons Limited, this Report has come into being.

When one hears, mainly through the media, arguments related to the greenhouse effect and global warming, too often, one only hears, in isolation, a one sided case for or against - a situation which does little to provide an informed view to assist the widening of public understanding of global environmental issues.

Many delegates and speakers at the Global Warming Debate have told me that they found the Debate informative, balanced and well structured. I believe all who read the edited versions of speeches made at the Debate will agree with these comments.

I am confident that discussions at the Global Warming Debate and this Report will be able to help decision makers reach responsible conclusions on global warming and influence environmental agendas within the foreseeable future.

STRATEGY EUROPE LTD. 60 BELTRAN ROAD, LONDON, SW6 3AJ

Tel: (International) +44 71 736 5976 (National) 071-736 5976   Telex:896691 TLXIR G: Ref: R913
Fax: (International) +44 71 731 6961 (National) 071-731 6961

ABOUT THE AUTHORS OF THE GLOBAL WARMING DEBATE

Strategy Europe Limited

STRATEGY EUROPE LIMITED (SE) is a Government/Parliamentary environment consultancy that conceives and develops national and international debates linked with waste management, the greenhouse effect and global warming.

On environmental issues, Strategy Europe advises institutions, corporations and charitable and voluntary agencies.

Apart from environmental issues, Strategy Europe has been active in representing clients in the area of telecommunications (IT), contracting out within the National Health Service, financial services and humanitarian programmes, particularly international famine relief.

Strategy Europe has planned for the following global warming debates over the next eighteen months following its conception of the Global Warming Debate at the Royal Society on the 7th and 8th March this year.

Global Warming: The Scientific Debate
Global Warming: The Economic Debate
Global Warming: The Media Response
Global Warming: The Transport Debate
Global Warming: The Energy Debate
Global Warming: The Framework Policy Debate
Global Warming: Legislation for the Environment
Global Warming: The Business Reponse
Global Warming: The East European Response
Global Warming: Food and Agriculture
Global Warming: Population Crisis
Global Warming: Aviation Impact
Global Warming: Investment - The Profit Factor.

Like the Global Warming Debate which this Report covers, the one day seminar debates will be aimed at specialists in given fields and speakers will be specialists on the subjects of each of the seminar debates.

The venues for these one day seminar debates are likely to be in London. If you would like details on these please let us know.

ACKNOWLEDGEMENTS

The following organisations have been kind enough to sponsor the Debate and this report:

Strategy Europe Limited

British Coal Corporation

The Directory of Public Affairs & Corporate Relations
(published by the Berkeley Press)

Environmental Resources Ltd

Intramark

Masons Solicitors

Nuclear Electric plc

PA Consulting Group

Shell International Petroleum Company Limited

AB Volvo

Yorkshire Electricity Group plc

CONTENTS

Contributors to the Volume   xv

Contributors' Biographies   xvii

Message from Gro Harlem Bruntland   xxvii

Keynote Address
Dr David Everest   1

Part I	THE SCIENTIFIC DEBATE	
1	The Case for the Greenhouse Effect Dr John T Houghton, CBE, FRS	7
2	Global Warming: Beyond the Popular Consensus Professor Patrick J Michaels	13
3	What Effect Might Deforestation Have on Global Climate? Dr Jane Goodall	21

Part II	THE ENERGY DEBATE	
4	The Continuing Need fro Energy and Alternative Energy Sources Helga Steeg	31
5	International Collaboration in Carbon Dioxide Collection and Disposal Professor John T. McMullan	37
6	Coal: A Positive Response from an Indispensable Fuel Malcolm J. Edwards	41
7	Nuclear Power: A Partner in Control Mark A. W. Baker	45
8	The Vital Role of Energy Efficiency in Reducing Carbon Dioxide Emissions Stewart T. Boyle	49

Part III	THE TRANSPORT DEBATE	
9	Issues for Action Michael C. L. Roberts	59
10	The Response of the Motor Industry to Environmental Pressure Sigvard Hoggren	63
11	The Need for Society to Move Towards Environmentally Sound Transport Andrew Davis	67

Part IV   FRAMEWORK POLICY AND LEGISLATION

12   The Response to Global Warming, the Policy Progress, IPCC and
Preparations for Climate Convention
Dr Pier Vellinga   75

13   A Framework for Survival: Moving Beyond the Current Approach
Dr Michael R. Redclift   79

14   International, National and Regional Legal Frameworks:
A New Concept in International Law
Malcolm Forster   85

Part V   THE ECONOMIC DEBATE

15   The Economic Implications of Global Warming
Nicholas J. Hartley   91

16   Can Eastern Europe Cope with Targets set by the West?
Professor Zdzislaw Kaczmarek   97

17   Preventive or Curative Action?
Donald H. Pearlman   101

Part VI   THE BUSINESS RESPONSE TO GLOBAL WARMING

18   The Industrial Sector's Voluntary Codes of Practice
Dr Horst Wiesebach   111

19   How Have Businesses Responded to Environmental Legislation?
David Jones   117

20   The Effect of Global Warming on Business
David R. Cope   121

21   Industry Action on Global Warming Issues
Christopher Hampson   125

CONTRIBUTORS TO THE VOLUME

Mark A. W. Baker
Nuclear Electric Plc

Stewart T. Boyle
Greenpeace International

David R. Cope
UK CEED

Andrew Davis
Environmental Transport Association

Malcolm J. Edwards, CBE
British Coal Corporation

Dr David A. Everest
UK CEED

Malcolm Forster
Freshfields

Dr Jane Goodall
The Jane Goodall Institute

Christopher Hampson
ICI Plc

Nicholas J. Hartley
Department of Environment

Sigvard Hoggren
AB Volvo

Dr John T. Houghton, CBE, FRS
The Meteorological Office

David Jones
Masons Solicitors

Professor Zdzislaw Kaczmarek
IIASA

Professor John T. McMullan
University of Ulster

Professor Patrick J. Michaels
University of Virginia

Donald H. Pearlman
Patton, Boggs and Blow

Dr Michael R. Redclift
Wye College

Michael C. Roberts
PA Consulting Group

Helga Steeg
International Energy Agency

Peter Thompson
Strategy Europe Limited

Dr Pier Vellinga
IPCC Response Strategies Working Group

Dr Horst P. F. Wiesebach
UNIDO

CONTRIBUTORS' BIOGRAPHIES

Mark Baker was born in 1940, educated at the University College of Rhodesia and Nyasaland and at Christ Church, Oxford, where he was a Rhodes scholar. He joined the United Kingdom Atomic Energy Authority (AEA) in 1964. He was appointed Secretary of AERE Harwell in July 1976. In April 1981 he took up an appointment at Risley as Director of Personnel and Administration of AEA's Northern Division. He returned to London Headquarters as Authority Personnel Officer in 1984, and became Secretary of the Authority in 1986. He joined the Central Electricity Generating Board in December 1989 as a Board Member (Designate) in Nuclear Electric Division and became Director for Corporate Affairs and Personnel in Nuclear Electric Plc on the company's formation in March 1990.

Stewart T. Boyle is Energy Policy and Research Director for Greenpeace International. Prior to that he was Director of the Energy and Environment Programme for the Association for the Conservation of Energy. He has also worked for Friends of the Earth as National Energy Campaigner. He has a degree in Geography and a postgraduate diploma in management studies. Before working for ACE he ran Friends of the Earth's energy campaign for four years. He is author of 'The Greenhouse Effect': A Practical Guide to the World's Changing Climate' (1989), 'Limiting Climate Change' (1990, as well as a wide range of reports and articles on energy and pollution matters.

David R. Cope is the Executive director of the UK Centre for Economic and Environmental Development (UK CEED). UK CEED is an independent research institute, based in Cambridge, UK, created in 1984 to explore the interactions between economic and environmental circumstances in the UK. Formerly with the International Energy Agency of the OECD, David Cope is a member of the UK Cabinet Office (Advisory Council on Science and Technology) Standing Committee on the Environment and chairman of its economic questions working group. He is also a member of several other government and independent advisory committees. He is the author of numerous books, reports and papers on various aspects of energy/environment interactions.

Andrew Davis read Urban Studies at the University of Kent, where he specialised in transport structures and land use patterns, and wrote his thesis on the fare structure of London Transport. On graduating in 1979 he joined the Greater London Council's Planning and Transportation Department and became a consultant for the GLC's Transport and Mobile Plant Fleet.

Malcolm J. Edwards has been in the British coal industry all his working life. After Cambridge he entered the National Coal Board as a graduate trainee, became Director General of Marketing in 1973 and Commercial Director and a member of the main Board in 1985. He is Chairman of the British Fuels Group and Deputy Chairman of Inter-continental Fuels.

Dr David A. Everest was formerly a Division Leader at the National Physical Laboratory in the field of material science and chemical standards, and from 1979-86 Chief Scientific Officer Environmental Pollution and Director of Environment Science Policy at the UK Department of the Environment. At present a Senior Research Associate at the UK Centre for Economic and Environmental Development, a Visiting Research Fellow in the Environmental Sciences Department at the University of East Anglia, and Editor of the journal Energy and Environment.

Malcolm Forster has recently joined the Environment Law Group of Freshfields after many years as Director of the Environmental Law Centre at the University of Southampton. He has particular responsibility for developing the firm's international environmental law practice. He has worked as a consultant on environmental law matters in the United Nations Environment Programme, the European Commission and the Organisation for Economic Co-operation and Development. He has written widely on environmental law matters and is the Managing Editor of The Land Management and Environmental Law Report.

Jane Goodall, born in London, fulfilled her childhood ambition when she was asked by the world renowned anthropologist, Louis Leakey, to study chimpanzees in Tanzania. Her research at Gombe National Park is now the longest continuous study of any animal in the wild. Today she spends much of her time travelling around the world attending conferences, lecturing, meeting heads of state and politicians, campaigning to save chimpanzees from extinction and to improve books and numerous children's stories, as well as many scientific papers. She has received a number of prestigious awards for her achievements.

Christopher Hampson is a Canadian who has worked in the ICI Group since 1956 when he joined Canadian Industries Ltd. He spent four years in ICI's head office in London as General Manager Planning, before becoming Managing Director of ICI Australia Limited in 1984. He was appointed an Executive Director of Imperial Chemical Industries PLC in September 1987 where his responsibilities include Safety, Health & Environment. He is a Non-Executive Director of Costain Group PLC and Hawker Siddeley Group PLC. He is Chairman of the CBI Environment Committee, and is also a member of the Business in Environment Target Team and of the UK Government's Advisory Committee on Business and the Environment.

Nicholas J. Hartley has been a member of the UK Government Economic Service since 1968. He has worked in a number of posts as an economic adviser including spells at the Treasury, the Central Policy Review Staff and the Office of Telecommunications (OFTEL). He joined the Department of the Environment in 1989 as Senior Economic Adviser in the Environment Protection Group. He heads a small team advising on all aspects of the economics of environment policies. The analysis of economic aspects of climate change has been an important part of this work.

Sigvard Hoggren is the Vice-President for Environmental Affairs with AB Volvo, Sweden. He joined Volvo in 1966, after working as a Regional School Superintendent in mid-Sweden. His present position includes corporate responsibility for initiating, coordinating and following-up environmental policies, planning and implementation, training procedures, audit and organization.

Dr John T. Houghton, FRS, has been Director General of the Meteorological Office since 1983, prior to which he was Deputy Director of the Rutherford Appleton Laboratory. He became Chief Executive of the new Meteorological Office Executive Agency in 1990. In 1988 Dr Houghton was appointed chairman of the Scientific Assessment Group of the Intergovernmental Panel on Climate Change. He is well known internationally for his outstanding research in remote sensing of the atmosphere from space. He is author of many books and scientific papers.

David Jones became an Equity Partner of Masons in May 1982. He has specialised in Building & Engineering disputes both here and abroad. He has dealt with the environmental implications of sea outfalls, sewerage treatment works, pipe-lines, hotels, hospitals, airports, roads and sugar silos. He also has considerable experience in insurance law. More recently he has tended to concentrate on environmental issues affecting certain industries including Construction, Paper and Chemical. He is one of a number of Partners in Masons dealing with various aspects of Environmental Law.

Zszislaw Kaczmarek has led the Water Resources Project at the International Institute for Applied Systems Analysis in Laxenburg, Austria since 1989. From 1981 to 1988 he was secretary General of the Polish Academy of Sciences and from 1961 to 1966 and 1976 to 1980 he was head of the Polish Hydrometeorological Service. In 1990 he was awarded the International Hydrology Prize.

Professor John T. McMullan is Director of the Centre of Energy Research, University of Ulster, Coleraine, Co. Londonderry, U.K., and Editor of the International Journal of Energy Research, published by John Wiley & Sons Ltd. He advises industry and government departments on energy policy and energy R&D. His research interests centre on the technical consequences of decisions to reduce CO_2 emissions, and on identification, characterisation and use of replacement for existing CFC and HCFC refrigerant working fluids.

Patrick J. Michaels is an Associate Professor of Environmental Sciences at the University of Virginia. Dr Michaels received his A.B. and S.M. Degrees at the University of Chicago in Biological Sciences and Plant Ecology. he was awarded a PhD in Ecological Climatology from the University of Wisconsin-Madison in 1979. Since that time he has been on the Faculty of the University of Virginia. He is also Virginia State Climatologist and was president of the American Association of State Climatologists in 1987-88. He served as the most recent Program Chair for the American Meteorological Society's Committee on Applied Climatology. Dr Michaels is author of over 100 scientific and popular publications on climate and its impact on living systems.

Donald H. Pearlman, a partner in the prestigious Washington, D.C. law firm of Patton, Boggs & Blow, has substantial experience in government and as an attorney on energy and environmental issues. As Executive Assistant to the U.S. Secretary of Energy (1982-85) and the U.S. Secretary of the Interior (1985-89), he was senior advisor in the development and implementation of those Departments' major energy and environmental policies and was a member of the Energy, Environment, and Natural Resources Working Group of the President's Domestic Policy Council. Mr Pearlman graduated from Havard University cum laude in economics and the Yale Univeristy School of Law.

Dr Michael R. Redclift is currently Research Coordinator of the Global Environmental Change Initiative of the UK Economic and Social Research Council. He is Reader in Rural Sociology at Wye College, University of London. Formerly he was Programmed Advisor for the Ford Foundation in Mexico City, where he helped establish a pioneering research programme in Resources and the Environment (1987-80). During the last ten years he has acted as a consultant to several international agencies on Sustainable Development, including the FAO and UNRISD (United Nations Research Institute for Social Development).

Michael C. Roberts is a Chemical Engineer, Director of PA Management Consultants and Director of Energy Management within the PA Consulting Group. Prior to joining PA some 8 years as a business consultant he founded and built up PA's significant energy and environment consulting activities. He regards energy as the major issue in the Global Warming debate. He is also a member of the Executive Council of the Parliamentary Group for Energy Studies, and President-Elect of the Institute of Energy.

Helga Steeg was appointed Executive Director of the International Energy Agency (IEA) in May 1984. She came to the Agency from the German Economics Ministry where, as a senior official, she dealt with trade and energy issues, foreign investment, and relations between industrialised and developing nations. At the IEA, Mrs Steeg has supported moves by Member governments to reduce barriers to trade in energy and to encourage competition between energy sources. Under her leadership, the IEA has improved and expanded its system for gathering and evaluating data on energy markets. It has also strengthened its analysis of environmental aspects of energy production and use.

Frederic P. Thompson (known as Peter) is an environmental public affairs consultant and Deputy Chairman of Strategy Europe Ltd. Prior to joining Strategy Europe Ltd he was Head of Public Affairs for Aims of Industry for some eight years and at the same time senior advisor to the Foundation for Business Responsibilities. He conceived and was director, in April 1990, of the International Conference on a Call for a National Environmental Waste Policy which took place in the House of Lords. For the Global Warming Debate, held at the Royal Society London (about which this report has been published) he was also author and director. He planned and directed the first National Conference on 'The Role of Public Affairs in Communications' (1986). He is a member of the Confederation of British Industry's Multinational Affairs Panel and also a member of the CBI's working party on the Greenhouse Effect. He is author of 'Social Responsibility and the Business Community' (1984). He is a Fellow of the Royal Society of Arts, an independent journalist as a member of the National Chartered Institute of Journalists, an associate journalist member of the London Foreign Press Association, and a Fellow of the Institute of Directors. He was on two occasions elected to the Council of the Institute of Public Relations.

Dr Pier Vellinga (1950) heads the Air Quality and Climate Change Division in the Ministry of Housing, Physical Planning and Environment in the Netherlands. He is also the Director of the National Climate Change Programme and in that capacity has developed the basis for a National Policy on Atmospheric Pollution and Climate Change. On behalf of the Netherlands, he is Vice-Chairman of the Response Strategies Working Group of the Intergovernmental Panel on Climate Change (IPCC). He has now joined the UN Negotiating Process for the Framework Convention on Climate Change. In 1989, he organised the Noordwijk Ministerial Conference on Atmospheric Pollution and Climatic Change. As the secretary to this Conference, he facilitated the drawing up of the Noordwijk Declaration through a process of international consultations and negotiations.

Horst P. F. Wiesebach in 1986 was appointed Deputy Director-General of the United Nations Industrial Development Organization (UNIDO) in charge of the Department for Programme and Project Development. At present he is charged with the preparations for UNIDO's Global Conference on Ecologically Sustainable Industrial Development (ESID) to be held in Copenhagen, 14-18 October 1991. Prior to this appointment, he was Assistant Administrator of the United Nations Development Programme in New York where he headed since 1980 the Bureau for Programme Policy and Evaluation. From 1977 to 1980 he was Director of the German Development Institute in Berlin and from 1971 to 1977, Division Chief at the Federal Ministry of Economic Co-operation in Bonn. He was born in Groschowitz (FRG) in 1934 and graduated from Philips University, Marburg, with a Ph.D. in Economics.

David Trippier and Peter Thompson

Earl of Shannon

Peter Thompson

Mark A. W. Baker

Stewart T. Boyle

David R. Cope

Andrew Davis

Malcolm J. Edwards

Dr David A. Everest

Malcolm Forster

Dr Jane Goodall

Christopher Hampson

Nicholas J. Hartley

Sigvard Hoggren

David Jones

Professor Zdzislaw Kaczmarek

Professor John T. McMullan

Professor Patrick J. Michaels

Donald H. Pearlman

Dr Michael R. Redclift

Michael C. Roberts

Helga Steeg

Dr Pier Vellinga

Dr Horst P. F. Wiesebach

MESSAGE FROM

Gro Harlem Brundtland
Prime Minister Of Norway

"The threats to our global environment have become even more alarming since the world Commission on Environment and Development presented its report 'Our Common Future' in 1987. The greenhouse effect is in the process of being significantly enhance by emission of human activities on earth. The threat of climate change has been moved from the back pages of scientific journals to newspaper headlines. The pace of deforestation, soil erosion and loss of species is increasing. Despite efforts to combat world poverty and to curve the growth of world population, the situation has become worse rather than better. These problems are all inter-linked and in no other area are these linkages stronger than in the debate on how to respond to the threat of global warming which is truly one of the most complex global issues facing us today. It involved several disciplines of science; it effects the very essence of life style and consumption patterns in the world economy; it constitutes a fundamental part of the economic life and industrial level of states and it goes to the core of the north-south relationship. We know that ecology and economy are inextricably linked and that environmental degradation can only be reversed by restructuring the economic system which has led us into the present crisis. We have begun the hard task of integrating the principles of sustainability into the way we run our society, from the level of the individual to that of the national and international decision making. We must integrate environmental concerns into all levels of economic planning, performance and accounting. A truly effective strategy for change must be built on a cradle-to-grave approach from scientific exploration, and technological innovation, through the cycles of production and consumption to emissions control and waste disposal. The World Commission pointed out the sharp contrast between the integrated and inter-dependent character of the new challenges facing us and the fragmented and limited nature of our responses. If we are to achieve real measurable progress in Brazil in 1992, we must deal with specific issues concerning environment and development aiming to achieve substantive and measurable progress in Rio. But we also take due account of the close inter-linkages between the problems concerned by arranging our work in a way which would enable us to arrive at more comprehensive responses. A comprehensive approach will be particularly important in the negotiations on a world climate convention which started in Washington in February. We must deal with the sources of emissions in the same context as we deal with the ability of nature to absorb them. I am pleased to note that the next rounds of negotiations will allow such an approach, which will enable us to reach agreements based on a more equitable sharing of burdens and to be more cost-effective in our choice of responses. Optimal results can be achieved with today's environmental agreements. The marginal costs of reducing emissions vary greatly from country to country, yet we have continued to adopt agreements based on the simple notion of equal percentage reduction, regardless of how this effects the total costs or, even more importantly, total results. In the new generation of environmental agreements, we must seek to achieve a maximum of environmental benefit at the minimum cost. CO_2 is the most important of the greenhouse gases and the most difficult to deal with. I believe we should develop agreements on the use of both international CO_2 charges and of tradeable CO_2 quotas. We should try to establish a global ceiling of emissions. Each country or region could then reduce emissions according to an emission quota within the global ceiling. This ceiling could subsequently be lowered. In our efforts to save the global environment, a special responsibility lies with the industrialised countries. We have drawn upon the natural capital left to us by our fore-fathers. We have paid little or none of the true environmental costs of our growth and we have passed on most of the bill to the generations coming after us. The industrialised countries must, therefore, assume the main burden of reducing the global level of emissions. This means that we must increase our technological and financial assessments to third world countries to enable them to take part in the global effort. All countries must commit themselves to appropriate efforts to combat global warming. Equity and efficiency must be combined in order to achieve optimal results which are acceptable to all parties concerned. Never have our knowledge and ability to address vital challenges been greater. Our generation has a unique responsibility and opportunity to manage global change and to do so in time.

Please accept my best wishes for a successful conference."

KEYNOTE ADDRESS

Dr David Everest

Senior Research Associate at the UK Centre for Economic Risk Assessment
Unit Development, Editor of 'Energy and Environment Research'

The approach I propose to adopt is to set out what I see as the key factors which influence the development and implementation of policy on the global warming issue. You may well not agree with my views, but I hope that their expression will help stimulate your own thinking, especially when you hear the authoritative speakers who are going to follow.

My first factor that I am going to take is the underlying science. As a scientist myself, I have put that at the top and I do believe that scientific factors are the first key in understanding the global warming issue. Policy makers are not necessarily particularly interested in understanding the detailed and very fascinating underlying science. What they are concerned about is understanding the scientific uncertainties. Uncertainties regarding future emissions of greenhouse gases; uncertainties regarding how the global warming will emerge, how fast it will emerge, how large it will be; uncertainties about a future climate variation from natural causes and how this compares with warming which we are obtaining from the greenhouse effect. Those are the kinds of uncertainties about which the policy maker needs advice.

In the UK, we would look to the Royal Commission on Environmental Pollution to provide this advice. Internationally, we have obviously to look to an international advisory committee and one has been set up with the Inter-governmental Panel on Climate Change, a very effective body and particularly Working Group 1 which covers the basic science. They have published their report and we are fortunate indeed in having Dr Houghton who is the Chairman of Working Group 1 to give us an authoritative account of their deliberations. Of course,

there will be those who have a different view to this scientific consensus developed by Working Group 1 and, again, we have Professor Michaels who will be speaking second in the debate. It will be very interesting to hear the contrast of these two speakers and their conclusions.

At the moment, I must say that I am going to take the results of Working Group 1 as being my own Bible for thinking on the greenhouse issue. A very large number of scientists have contributed, working scientists and well-known scientists from all areas of the globe, so there is no question of just the west or the undeveloped countries being represented. At the moment, I will take that personally as giving a view of the scientific consensus. But, of course, that scientific consensus can change.

That is the first of my issues and, I believe, the most important. The next is almost as important, in fact for many reasons, almost more important. That is the impact of public perception. In a democracy it is public perception which eventually makes its views felt through the applicable machinery which will govern the development of environmental policy. It is very important, therefore, to try and understand and see how public perception will develop on the greenhouse issue.

If we take the developed world, and the UK particularly, certainly in the last two to three years, public interest in the greenhouse effect has multiplied very greatly and very unexpectedly. I am, however, not clear how far this is a pointed interest in the greenhouse and the global warming issue, and how much just reflects a general increase in interest in environmental questions generally. I would rather suspect that, if stringent economic measures were brought forward, the public support in the advanced

Global Warming: The Debate
Edited by Peter Thompson with the assistance of John P. O'Hara
© 1991 Strategy Europe Ltd. Published 1991 by John Wiley & Sons Ltd.

countries may not be quite so strong as people are now thinking. That is my guess, and this would be reinforced by the feeling that, for example, the consequences of global warming do not appear awfully unpleasant for countries in the middle to high latitudes where most of the economically advanced countries are placed. I am quite relaxed over the possibility of growing maize in Scotland, or citrus fruit and grapes in England.

Possibly, concern may be generated in the advanced countries as the populations start to associate the effects of natural disasters. These we are vividly shown by the media: floods in Bangladesh, famine in East Africa, and if the populations start to associate these natural disasters with the global warming then, possibly, this could be a trigger which will increase public concern sufficiently in advanced countries to really support drastic measures.

If we look at the developing countries, the public perception will be different:

(1)   The first point about public perception in these countries is that they will be determined not to put anything in the way of their economic development. The growth of industry, the growth of agriculture, they will see as inviolate and absolutely essential for their well-being.

(2)   Secondly, they will quite rightly point out that the present global warming is a problem which is associated primarily with the developed world: CO_2 emission from the economically advanced countries of something in the order of 5 tonnes of carbon per capita a year, compared with emissions of around 0.2 to 0.6 tonnes of carbon per capita in a developed world. Therefore, they will say that action must first be taken by the economically advanced countries and, indeed, these countries should also provide financial assistance for the developing world to take up CO_2 friendly technologies.

You have this contrast in public perception and these differences of public perception will have to be allowed for in negotiations on future global warming policy.

The media has a major role in helping the public to understand the effects of environmental prob-

lems. It also plays a significant role in the reverse, in enabling the government to put forward views and spread the message to the population at large.

Generally, the media can be very effective putting over the facts of environmental problems. Where they probably tend to fall down, in my view, and it is a very difficult area, is in representing the scientific uncertainties which are associated with environmental issues. This is important because the public yearns for certainty, and certainty is not there. The policy-maker must make his decisions in the light of uncertainties and it would be very good if the public could start to understand how these uncertainties arise.

Now my next two factors. Firstly we will deal with restrictions on CO_2 emissions. I am dealing here with restrictions on emissions from possible fossil fuel combustion which is, undoubtedly, the major man-made impact of carbon dioxide into the atmosphere. Of course, if we could find some means of extracting carbon dioxide from flue gases and, even more importantly, finding somewhere to put it so that it is actually out of the climate systems, then that would transform our whole approach to the global warming issue. Personally, I am rather pessimistic about the chances of this coming about, but I am hopeful that my pessimism will prove unfounded.

In the meantime, however, we have to actually tackle methods for reducing the emission of carbon dioxide which means essentially reducing fossil fuel use and this is undertaken by two main methods:

– either by increasing energy use efficiency, or

– by moving to non-fossil fuel emitting technologies.

Increased energy efficiency has always been a subject which governments have tended to favour. Certainly the UK government has supported measures, for many years, to increase energy efficiency throughout the economy. Since 1983, this task has fallen on the Energy Efficiency Office. Increasing energy use efficiency is an important tool for controlling greenhouse emissions. It is one of the tools which we will have to adopt. My only doubt, and I have a small doubt here, is how far this increased energy use efficiency will feed through into actual reductions of fossil fuel use and how much will feed through into increased economic output. An increase in economic output is a perfectly worthy and satisfactory outcome, but we may not get quite the reductions in fossil fuel use that we might expect because we will in actual fact get greater economic growth instead.

How about changing energy supply? This is already starting, particularly there is an increased use of natural gas throughout the economy. Natural gas gives half as much CO_2 as combustion of oil or coal for a different amount of energy and as it is also environmentally clean and, at the moment, not overly expensive there are both economic and environmental reasons for increasing natural gas burn. If natural gas remains in good supply, I cannot see anybody wishing to settle to build a coal fire power station with the necessity of putting expensive fuel gas desulphurisation equipment on it. But, of course, natural gas may not remain in such free supply as some suggest. It is, in the short term, a very effective means of reducing CO_2 emissions with relation to energy supply.

At some stage, we will have to go beyond it. We will have to move to increased use of non-fossil fuel sources and the problem here is that we run into another set of environmental problems. The two technologies which can most quickly give us CO_2 free energy are nuclear power and hydro power, and both are centres of strong opposition. Nuclear power on safety and social concerns and its relation to military applications. Hydro power because of its high land use intensity. This involves often loss of wildlife habitat and of human habitats and often does give rise to very intense local opposition. I would suggest that similar oppositions are likely to emerge as other renewable energy procedures start to grow: wind power (a large number of turbines), use of biomass (special crops), the Severn barrage – all of these can lead to environmental problems. It does seem to me that one of the important things we must do is to consider how we can overcome these environmental concerns and political oppositions to these methods because I do not see how we can get significant reductions in CO_2 emissions

without adoption of non-fossil fuel technologies.

The fourth issue is deforestation. To increase deforestation or preferably even reverse it is a most desirable environmental end, not only ecologically – and there are very strong ecological arguments for doing so – but also because it undoubtedly will make some contribution to stabilising CO_2 emissions, although not as great in my view as limiting fossil fuel use.

However, the reduction in deforestation is a policy which will appeal much more to the economically advanced countries than it will to the developing world. The developing countries look upon their forests as major economic resources necessary for their development and, not only that, they do provide an economic resource which can be developed immediately to meet what they see as pressing demands for their often very poor populations. They will, therefore, not take kindly to being instructed that they have to adopt policies against deforestation. These pressures do not hold for the economically advanced countries who have either already destroyed their forests, or if they do have forests they manage them quite satisfactorily on a renewable basis. They do not have that concern.

I would suggest that all those concerned in greenhouse policy and its formulation, policy makers, industrialists and the greens, do not push the deforestation issue to an extent as treating it as a soft option. This has been treated as a soft option in the advanced countries because the action always falls on other people and it enables you not to take what are often unpalatable decisions domestically. But that does not mean that deforestation is, in its own right, good.

My fifth issue is the economic and political implications of CO_2 reduction targets which, from the point of view of this conference are important.

At present, it is the OECD countries and the centrally planned economies who are responsible for the majority of global CO_2 emissions. However, this will not last. As the developing world increases its standard of living and faces up to its rapidly increasing population, their energy demand must rise. I would suggest that this energy demand is almost certainly going to be met by conventional fossil fuel technology. It does not seem likely that the developing world has either the financial resources, the technical resources or the land resources necessary for the large scale development of non-fossil fuel energy technologies. Therefore, we are going to be faced with an increase in CO_2 output from the developing world, possibly quite rapidly. This clearly will have to be balanced by an extra decrease in CO_2 emissions from both the developing and the centrally planned economies if we are going to get an overall global CO_2 reduction.

The problem comes down quite shortly to this:

(1) The targets for the economically advanced countries must not entail such large economic penalties as to damage their wealth generating capacity and, in particular, to lose the support of their populations.

(2) CO_2 reduction targets must not interfere with the ability of the centrally planned economies to move towards a market economy, especially in Eastern Europe, where this movement is taking place rapidly.

(3) The developing world will have to have targets which will allow them to develop industrially and still meet their full objectives.

That is probably the centre-piece of the global warming political debate and, I suggest, it is a very important part of this conference to look at this particular problem.

My last three factors are transport, adaptation and population trends. I cannot cover all of these here so I will just look at the last two.

Adaptation particularly is an important issue because we will, almost certainly, have to adopt some adaptation methods, either because global warming is larger than we expected in which case we will have no choice but to adapt – we will not be able to move fast enough – or, possibly, if global warming is quite slight, then adaptation will be by far the most effective overall response. Even if we fall somewhere between the two, adaptation may allow us to reduce the adverse economic impacts of greenhouse policies and make room for a political agreement amongst nations.

What we do need, I would suggest, is to understand the science of the greenhouse effect more effectively in order that we can really understand what are the opportunities and limitations of adaptation. That is an area which I think we should pay attention to.

Finally, world population trends. May I just remind you of the United Nation figures:-

World population:

2.5 billion	– 1985
5 billion	– Now
billion	– 2020 – 2030
14 billion	– Next Century

Already 45% of the world's population live in cities and that percentage will almost certainly increase, probably up to 70% by 2030. People who live in cities require work, they are going to work in industry, they are going to require transport, they are going to require all those environmental services which already the urban communities are finding so hard to provide. I would suggest that, if the developing world's increased population want a reasonable living standard, then it is probably going to be nearly impossible to solve current environmental problems, including global warming along the presently envisaged lines. That has to be seriously considered. Indeed, unrestrained population growth is probably the most important issue actually facing the world's governments.

One final thought: we need to restrict population growth and there is only one way which has been undertaken effectively, and that is in the Western World and in the OECD countries whose populations have levelled off and that is associated with economic development. It does appear that economic development is the only proven method so far of limiting populations. All other options, such as stringent control on parenthood, look pretty unattractive. This may be an area where industry can contribute because, if industry can foster sustainable economic growth and thereby increase economic well-being and thereby lead to limitation of population by this effect, then it probably could make a most important contribution to containment of the environmental effects generally and the global warming effects in particular.

Part I

The Scientific Debate

1

THE CASE FOR
THE GREENHOUSE EFFECT

Dr John T. Houghton

Chief Executive, Meteorological Office Executive Agency

In this particular debate the science is absolutely basic. It was two years ago, in November 1988, when the Intergovernmental Panel on Climate Change was formed as a joint body between the World Meteorological Organisation and the United Nations Environment Programme.

It was a very timely formation of a body because, at that time, the whole problem of global warming had begun to evolve; our own Prime Minister had made her famous speech to this particular Society in which she spelled out some of the problems of greenhouse warming. That body formed three Working Groups, the first Working Group was on science, which I chaired, the second on impact, and the third on policy. It is the results of that first Working Group which I would like to present to you rather briefly.

We had to work fast and rather hard and the brief, of course, was to make sure that we involved as many scientists in the world as possible, and that we took the best possible advice. It was a truly international procedure involving about two hundred scientists in writing the drafts of the chapters, we held twelve international workshops, and we sent the document drafts out for review by a further two hundred scientists to check what comments they sent back.

We had two important meetings, one a meeting of lead authors, together with some other scientists – about sixty in total – and then a meeting of the Working Group which is a delegate body attended by delegates from nearly one hundred countries and we argued loud and long over our findings. In the end, there was no dissension from our wording of

the final report, nor have I received any correspondence since complaining about any of the wording of that final report, despite the many arguments we had and, of course, despite the uncertainties which surround it. We believe, therefore, that we have something of a scientific consensus and I will say more about that in a moment.

There was, at the beginning of this exercise, a lot of discussion amongst the key scientific community about the sort of report we should produce. Our own office was keen that we presented a report which could be understood well by policy makers and by others who had no scientific background, and that we owed it to that community to explain clearly what we believe we know, what our best estimates were, and what the uncertainties are. Some scientists, perhaps many scientists to begin with, were unhappy about that and because they felt that we did not know enough to make any estimates at all and that we should really tell the world that we do not know. There are still some scientists who feel in that particular way. There are scientists, of course, on the other end of the spectrum who felt that we were being far too weak in our report and that we should be much more positive and emphasise very much more the possible deleterious effects of global warming. So, we found ourselves somewhere in the middle of this body of scientists.

In trying to put forward an estimate for the future, what we are doing is producing something like a weather forecast and the instruction to forecasters, who forecast the weather for tomorrow, is that they should explain what the story is, what they believe the weather is most likely to do tomorrow. It is no

Global Warming: The Debate
Edited by Peter Thompson with the assistance of John P. O'Hara

good for them to say 'it may rain, it may snow, it may hail, it may be sunny, it may be warm, it may be cold' – they may cover all the possibilities by that and make sure they protect their back sides – but they are not putting any information over to the public. The maximum information is put over when they just describe what they believe the most likely events are going to be.

I believe we had something like a similar task in forecasting the climate for the next century. We had to come up with what our best estimate was and that we tried to do. In the case of the weather forecast, you have no need to explain to the public what the uncertainties are. They have plenty of experience of that, because they experience weather forecasts every day. But in forecasting for a hundred years, of course, we have no experience of that and it is also very important to explain the uncertainties. I believe that, in the report which we have produced, we have explained what we know and what we do not know.

The scientific debate, of course, goes on and it is natural that it should. The very essence of science is that there should be debate and that people should argue and discuss and try to ascertain just what the truth is. Therefore, we cannot expect to have complete consensus, although I believe we have come to something like that.

(1) **What is the greenhouse effect?**

It occurs because there is an atmosphere above the earth's surface. That atmosphere, when it is clear, is largely transparent to solar radiation, but it is largely opaque to long wave radiation emitted by the surface. Radiation which is emitted by the surface is trapped by the atmosphere above and re-emitted in return and so keeps the earth's surface warm. The glass in the greenhouse works in something like the same fashion, hence the name 'greenhouse effect', although in some ways it is also a misnomer.

(2) **How do we know this greenhouse effect is real?**

First of all, we believe we understand the basic physics and, indeed, we can calculate that the earth's surface, at the moment, is kept at about 33°C warmer than it would be if this mechanism was not present. That number is one which is well established and is not, I think, open to much question. We can further apply the same sort of theory to the planet's Mars and Venus which have atmospheres which are almost pure CO_2. Mars has a very thin atmosphere and has about 10C of greenhouse warming. Venus has an extremely thick atmosphere of about one hundred earth's atmospheres of carbon dioxide – very deep indeed. This surface temperature of Venus is heated at about 500C because of the greenhouse effect. So the basic physics of the greenhouse warming is well known.

Further, we can go back in climatic history and as we go back over the last 160,000 years, we can find out what the average temperature of the earth has been over this period. And, by looking at ice cores, we can also see what the CO_2 content has been over that period by looking at gas trapped in ice cores. We find that the CO_2 during the period tracked extraordinarily well with the temperature curve. That, of course, does not prove anything because it may well be that the effect is the other way round and CO_2 content depends on temperature and, certainly, part of the story is that effect. We cannot model climates of the past with computer models (I will mention those later) unless we also assume that CO_2 acts as a greenhouse gas and induces warming in the atmosphere. Certainly some of the effects of the past is due to that and the amount which you deduce roughly ties in well with the sort of estimates we make otherwise.

(3) **What about the greenhouse gases?**

There is CO_2, methane, CFCs, Freons and some other which I will not mention in this talk. Carbon dioxide is the most important. It comes, as we know, from fossil fuel combustion, from deforestation. Methane comes from a variety of sources thought largely to be rice paddy fields, animal husbandry – cows emit methane from both ends – coal and gas mining and landfills are also sources of methane, and they track very well. The concentration of true methane tracks very well with the increase in human population. CFCs you will know from the ozone problem and they are now being controlled, of course, through the Montreal Protocol.

If we go back over the last hundred and fifty years or so, since the beginning of the industrial revolution, carbon dioxide has increased by 25% to 30%, methane has almost doubled, and CFCs were almost unknown before that in the atmosphere and they have gone up enormously. As I say, however, they are now controlled by the Montreal Protocol.

If we take greenhouse gases as emitted in 1990, how do they rate in their importance, their contribution to greenhouse warming? CO_2 is giving us about two thirds of the effect, methane something of the order of 20% and CFCs just over 10%. So CO_2 is by far the most important of these greenhouse gases.

An important consideration is the lifetime of the gases. If a gas goes into the atmosphere and it is immediately destroyed, then it does not matter too much because it does not remain there. The gases with the long lifetimes are those of most concern. Carbon dioxide has a rather complicated lifetime which is one or two hundred years. The CFCs have a lifetime of about one hundred years. Methane has a lifetime, which is much shorter, of about ten years, and the CFCs replacements – please note, the HCFCs and others are also greenhouse gases – they are shorter lived and, therefore, less of a problem, but if they are produced in sufficient quantities they could become a problem in the future.

This means that if we want to stabilise the amounts of gases and stop them rising, then we would have to cut the emissions of CO_2 by about 60% at the moment, we would have to cut methane emissions by a much smaller amount (because the lifetime is shorter) by 20%, and the CFCs again by about 70% or 80%.

In order to try to come up with an estimate as to how climate may change, we had to work on various emission scenarios. These were provided for us by Working Group 3 and, just to explain briefly what they are, the 'business as usual' Scenario ('A') assumes that we carry on burning fossil fuels and increasing human population without any real controls. It is a fairly realistic curve, at least for the first few years of the next century, and fits in well with what nations are projecting for their use of fossil fuels over this period. Scenario 'B', 'C' and 'D' are assuming greater controls over greenhouse gas emissions.

We can convert those emissions into concentrations in the atmosphere. Only under scenario 'D' do we actually get any stabilisation of gas in the atmosphere by the end of the next century. Under 'Business as usual' the amount of gases continues to grow well towards the end of the next century and well into the century beyond. But aren't we going to run out of fuel? The answer is no, we have enough coal to last for well over a thousand years at current rates of burning. Gas and oil reserves are still being found, but we certainly know that there is enough coal there to burn and to keep us going.

We made some estimates as to what effects would occur on global climate. I will mention the models and the uncertainties in the models a little later on but, first of all, what about the results?

The suggestion from the models is that, by 1990, we should have seen about .6 of a degree of warming from the pre-industrial period. Have we actually seen that in the climatic record? To the best of our knowledge, over that period, it has warmed up a bit, by about 1/2 a degree. But it shows a lot of fluctuations. The time when the maximum warming occurred was earlier this century and cannot have been due to greenhouse warming in particular, and we know that the climate system has a lot of variability in it. We know from the past climatic history and we know from just running models, that there is variability arising from inter-actions between the atmosphere and the ocean, between the atmosphere and the ice, and we expect these natural fluctuations to occur. These actual fluctuations are noise, but we have not yet seen the signal above the noise, nor should we have necessarily have expected to do so. We are not saying in our reports, in any way, that we believe in greenhouse warming because we have seen it. We believe the climatic record is not inconsistent with greenhouse warming over this period, but it is certainly no proof of it.

What about the sort of warming we are talking about by the year 2040 when the equivalent amount of CO_2 will have doubled. We are talking of around 1.5° between now and then. You might say that 1.5° is not very much, after all the temperature fluctuates day by day by much more than that and, between winter and summer, by tens of degrees celsius. Why are we worried about 1.5°? This is 1.5° in global average that we are talking about and the difference in global average temperature between the ice age and the intervening warm period is around 5 or 6°. When you are talking about 1.5's in global average temperature, you are talking of a quarter of an ice age. It is, therefore, really a big climate change and we have to understand that this change in the average can mean quite large changes in the extremes and that will be the biggest impact of climate change.

Under Scenario ('A') by 2100 we are talking of an increase of something like 3° which is very large in climatic terms.

What people looking at impact want to know is not what the global average is, but how the regional changes of climate might be. We have tried to look at that, but the models are much less good at predicting regional change. They are much less consistent in their predictions, so we are not putting a great deal of confidence in these. However the models do demonstrate fairly clearly that over the Great Plains of North America and over Southern Europe, although we have increased rain fall overall, there will be a decrease in summer rain fall, an increase in temperature and an increase in evaporation which would mean a decrease in soil moisture, an increase in periods of drought and a substantial effect on agriculture. The monsoon region of Asia would probably see greater rain fall on the average, greater flooding, and that could have a substantial effect on the agriculture of that region. For the Sahel region and Australia which were two other regions we studied, there was no unequivocal response from the models.

Another impact is sea level rise. In a warmer world, the sea level will rise just because the earth expands. It expands because it gets warmer and that is the largest single factor which occurs. We are talking of a total of around 60cm by the end of the next century. Sea level rise is also caused by glaciers melting and they have been melting for some time, and we project that they would increase melting in the next century in this warmer world. The ice caps, on the other hand, have a smaller contribution, in particular Antarctica which would probably grow. It would still, of course, be very cold and because it would be slightly warmer than before, there would be an increase in snow fall, an increase of water vapour and, therefore, an increase in concentration of ice which would be greater than around the sides of the Continent. The models show that Antarctica is likely to grow, Greenland is likely to get a bit

smaller and the net contribution from the ice caps, is about zero.

You can imagine that there is a lot of uncertainties on these estimates, but our estimate is about two thirds of a metre, as I say, by the end of the next century. You may say that that does not sound very large, it will only just begin to worry the Thames Barrier by that stage in London but, if you live in Bangladesh or the Nile Delta and you live less that two metres above sea level, then you would be very worried about two thirds of a metre sea level rise because you are likely to have to move your home. Millions of people live in such areas in those highly populated parts of the world.

Those are the estimates we have made as to what is likely to occur in the next century. So what about other factors? Many people in the world have talked about other factors that might change the climate.

The sun may change and may vary. We know that the sun has varied in the past. The cause of the ice age has been change in distribution of solar radiation due to astronomical changes in the earth's orbit and, if you try to take those into account and think what those might be over fifty years, then you come up with very small numbers. Over longer periods, of course, they become bigger, but over this period of say fifty or one hundred years, they are small. Volcanos – unless we get a very big increase in volcanic activity, the likely change of climate due to volcanic activity is again very small.

Another factor is 'manmade sulphur'. There is some speculation which is being discussed in literature at the moment, the possibilities that man may be changing the climate because of putting sulphates into the atmosphere from burning the fossil fuels. The sulphates act as very good condensation nuclei, they help clouds to form droplets, so with lots of sulphates around you get many smaller drops in clouds rather than few large drops. A cloud of lots of smaller drops in it has a higher albedo, a bigger reflectivity than a cloud with large drops and, therefore, we are losing energy to the system and that effect would tend to cool the system. Similarly, of course, if we start taking the sulphur out of fossil fuel emissions, we will reduce the amount of sulphate and conceivably the clouds would have larger drops and, therefore, we would be increasing the energy to the system. It could work both ways, depending on whether we are putting more sulphur in or less sulphur in.

The amount of experimental evidence to support this is not very large. There is certainly a question as to whether it is a really global effect or not. It is probably only present in the Northern Hemisphere and certainly not in the Southern Hemisphere because the sulphates do not get there in any quantities. The best estimates we made as a group of the possible effects due to that factor over a fifty year period, allowing for increased burning of fuels are well below the effect due to greenhouse warming from the models which we have used.

Why are the predictions uncertain?
They are uncertain because we do not know what the future emissions are because that depends on energy policy and so on. That may be changed in the light of people's perceptions of greenhouse warming. We have some problem in turning emissions into greenhouse gas concentrations because the sources and sinks are uncertain, but that is not a large uncertainty compared with others in our projections.

Feedbacks in climate models are the big source of uncertainty, especially the cloud radiation feedback as we do not know how to put clouds into models at the moment. The oceans also have a big effect. The timing of climate change is important.

The models which we use have to take into account all the interactions in the climate system which are very complex. The climate system consist of the atmosphere, which consists of gases, motions, clouds, water vapour and so on. The physics and dynamics have to be described in the models. The physics and dynamics of the oceans in a similar way have to be described, and the coupling between the two needs to be put into the models, as do the coupling with the land and the ice. Most of the feedbacks which occur here are what we call non-linear. In other words, you cannot add them up like a simple sum. They all interact with one another. If you try to use simple physical arguments to try to explain how the feedbacks might work, you can get it completely wrong because you have not got all the interactions into place. The only way we know, the only

tool we have to put all those interactions in, in a physically, mathematically and dynamically consistent manner, is the use of the numerical model and that is why we are so keen on using these tools. They are only tools of course – the information we get out is only as good as the information we put in – but they are a marvellous way of integrating the physics, the dynamics and to some extent the chemistry of the problem. They are, of course, the tools we use for forecasting the weather each day with increasing skill as the models get increasingly good.

Just to give you some idea of the feedback effect, if we have no feedback at all – in other words, if you just increase the amount of CO_2 and you have no other effect on the atmosphere, the clouds and everything else remains the same – the increase for doubling of CO_2 is around 1.2° in global temperature. Water vapour increases, however, in the warmer world and we are fairly sure that water vapour feedback would add about 40% or 50% to that number. Ice would then melt, and because ice and snow reflects sunlight and as they disappear, so more energy gets into the system. That is another positive feedback, and the combination of those three now something like doubles the basic number.

Clouds are the big problem and models on the different sorts of clouds parameterisations show variation over about a factor of three and much of the variation between our high curve and our low curve occurs because we do not really know with any certainty what the effects of the clouds are.

How do we know these models are right?
They are checked against existing climates in order to try to check the models against reality. If we cannot simulate the current climate then we cannot expect to simulate the changed climate. We compare the Meteorological Office model for sea level pressure over the globe with the observed summer sea level pressure. There is good agreement between the average circulation of the atmosphere as simulated from the model and, of course, all summers are not the same either in the real atmosphere or the model. We can simulate quite well all the main features of the total system by models.

We have attempted to simulate the climate about six thousand years ago. The problem with doing that is that we do not have too much information about it. By putting in what we know about the variation of radiation, the variation of CO_2 and the variation of ice over that period, we can simulate reasonably well what that climate was over that very different period. It is this sort of confidence we have got from running models to simulate current climate, and to simulate past climate that gives us some confidence that we can actually use them to simulate climate of the future.

So what is the feeling of the scientific community regarding greenhouse warming? As I have explained, we do not know in any great detail what the changes are likely to be in the warmer world and we have some uncertainty over the magnitude of it. However, if we plot the rate of change next century against the temperature rise over a given period and we can choose any reasonable period, like a hundred years or five hundred years, then all the changes in the past are well away from the rate of change that we are predicting, the mean prediction for the next century under the 'business as usual' scenario. It is only until you get to scenario 'D' that you get anywhere near the sort of rate of change we have had in the past.

The message from our report is that if our estimates are correct, then the climate change in the next century is likely to be considerably larger than it has ever been over the last ten thousand years and probably over the last hundred thousand years.

Further, the rate of change is likely to continue to increase unless we do something about it, not only next century, but the next century afterwards. If we want to stabilise the temperature change then we could, for instance, take a 2% reduction of CO_2 emissions after the year 2000 and, assuming the other gases are not controlled, that would begin to stabilise the temperature by the end of the next century by perhaps 1.5° above present levels.

I think I can speak for the scientific community represented by the people who contributed to the report – how do well feel about the uncertainties? We feel that the uncertainties are such that we cannot expect the world to suddenly take immediate drastic action which would be very expensive and would create a great deal of problems in itself. On the other hand, we do believe that, if the estimates we have made are good and realistic ones, we should make some effort now to slow down the rate of change by trying to freeze emissions of greenhouse gases in the way that, for instance, the EEC has done, Japan has done, and other countries. We should prepare over this period, over the next ten or fifteen years while we are trying to improve the estimates that the scientists are making, for what the climate change will be. Prepare for the more drastic action that we believe is likely to be needed in the next century in order to bring down the total rate of climate change and then stabilise it in the future so that the atmosphere does not run away so far as its temperature or its climate is concerned.

2

GLOBAL WARMING:
BEYOND THE POPULAR CONSENSUS

Professor Patrick J. Michaels

University of Virginia

Mr Jefferson, who wrote the 'Declaration of Independence' and founded the University of Virginia, also wrote in the publication called 'Notes on the State of Virginia' that the sea breeze used to penetrate inland to Williamsburg. Nowadays, he wrote, it gets to Richmond and some day it may reach all the way to the mountains. No doubt as the land is further cleared, it will move further westward. Jefferson apprehended the possibility that human economic activity was in fact capable of changing the climate of large regions. Of course, he was dead wrong about the sea breeze. He also wrote that government should be guided by science. In many places in his writings, you see his appeal to the age of reason and the enlightenment to guide public policy. I often think of the global warming problem knowing that the cost of a major intervention entails probably a great curtailment in the freedoms that he fought so dearly for and I think that is something that we ought to think about as we proceed through the discussion of global warming.

Now it is often said that there is a monolithic consensus of scientists on global warming – there is not. There is, however, the usual process of science that is going on this issue. There is a dynamic tension between empiricists and dynamicists – between inductive and deductive reasoners that has characterised scientific debates through history. This tension is very healthy because it is that tension which gives us the increase in knowledge we need so much.

Unfortunately, in my opinion, in the global warming issue, that tension has been exploited and erroneously politicised and that tension is being observed under the microscope of public scrutiny so that the rhetoric on this issue begins to expand far beyond the levels of scientific confidence.

There is an additional consensus on this issue which I would like to call a popular consensus or the popular vision. I believe that is what is driving a lot of this issue. The popular vision is a sea level rise of a metre or two, deserts in the Mid-Western United States and tidal waves lapping against the sky scrapers of Manhattan. That is not the scientific vision.

To give you an idea of how ensconced the popular vision is, on 23rd June 1988 James Anderson from NASA testified in front of two congressional committees that the current temperatures, meaning the temperatures of the 1980's, were not inconsistent with human alterations of the atmosphere. He never said that the drought of 1988 in the USA was caused by the greenhouse effect. CNN ran a poll two nights later and asked the question – yes/no – if the drought of 1988 was caused by the human greenhouse effect. 72% of the respondents said yes. Not one scientist that I know ever said that the drought of 1988 was caused by human greenhouse alteration.

There is a popular vision that this is already occurring and I submit to you that that vision is driven primarily by people who have a great deal of political interest.

As scientists, we have to tell the truth. This is one half of a quote by a scientist in the global warming issue. It says:

"On one hand we are ethically bound to scientific method, in effect promising to tell the truth, the whole truth and nothing but."

Global Warming: The Debate
Edited by Peter Thompson with the assistance of John P. O'Hara
© 1991 Strategy Europe Ltd. Published 1991 by John Wiley & Sons Ltd

Nothing truer could be said and Mr Jefferson, I am sure, would agree. Lester Brown from the Worldwide Institute wrote that getting on the path to prevent climatic change depends upon a wholesale reordering, a fundamental restructuring of the world's economy. I believe that is probably true too given some of the estimates of costs that I have seen.

Look at world population: the explained variance of atmospheric CO_2 concentration by population is 99%.

To reduce emissions to the point that we do not create a massive warming under some scenario requires engineering a point that is far, far off the population growth curve and will surely take a great deal of effort.

Here are some things that everyone agrees with: carbon dioxide concentration of the atmosphere is going up. When measurements were first made, in Mauna Loa it was about 350 and is currently about 354 parts per million. At the beginning and prior to the industrial revolution it was about 270 parts per million or about 25% below the current value.

The relative warming contribution of the various human emissions is agreed. Carbon dioxide is obviously about 50% of the overall enhancement. The next most important is methane caused primarily by rice paddy agriculture and bovine flatulence. Next is nitrous oxide thought to be the product of high intensity agriculture. Now consider the three inputs that I have just discussed. Consider it from the point of view just of one nation. The United States produces a large amount of carbon dioxide. The most efficient producer of carbon dioxide per BTU is coal which is a major source of domestic energy and export in the United States. The next two are thought to be the result of high intensity agriculture: the major source of light product export from the United States. There is clearly a great deal of economic well being at stake as we proceed through this.

Most interestingly, because of the contribution of all those gases, we have not really raised the CO_2 concentration from 270 or 280 to 354 but, in fact, from 270 to about 425 parts per million effectively. This is corroborated in the IPCC report. If you multiply the numbers, this is what you get.

If the earth's atmosphere were in equilibrium with the climate, according to a series of climate models run in the mid-1980's the earth's surface temperature should have gone up over 2 °C, but it is obviously not in equilibrium because of oceanic thermal lag and some other considerations. Even very conservative estimates of that suggest the Earth should have warmed considerably.

One of the series of five 'big' climate models that I believe fuelled a great deal of Congressional testimony in the US, and a great deal of popular vision of that, was that of the National Centre for Atmospheric Research. For winter time it predicted massive warming in December, January, February in the high latitudes of the Northern Hemisphere – 16°C. These are extremely large numbers and, given the fact that we are already half way to an effective doubling of carbon dioxide, one would think that one would begin to see some very large numbers emanating from those high latitudes.

Take a look at the temperature history. In the Jones and Wigley (East Anglia) temperature history for the southern hemisphere, (this is the half of the globe that is almost all water at its surface) the net increase in temperature over this century is about seven tenths of a degree celsius. Much of the increase occurred prior to 1945. That is why I make the statement that the warming in early Twentieth Century probably had little relation to this human greenhouse. If it did, it would be warmer than heck now and we would not be having this discussion.

The Southern Hemisphere has warmed up this much which is obviously underneath or at the very low end of main projections and the answer that is often given is that oceanic thermal lag will be holding it back. Let us consider that and let us take a look at another problem.

A satellite record from 1979, through 1990, over the Southern Hemisphere shows no net change in these temperatures. Why do the Southern Hemisphere temperatures as measured by ground based thermometers show an increase? This suggests that there is a warm bias in the land based records over the last decade plus a couple of years, in the order of one to two tenths of a degree celsius. Many people think that this could be because of the urban effect: cities are growing up around their thermometers. There is no doubt that population has been increasing and this effect has confounded records for a long time. One would come to the conclusion that if the warmest years were not at the end of the record, we would have real problems and the Earth would probably be cooling.

The Southern Hemisphere, it is often said, does not warm up very much because it is all water. Most climate models retard warming in that Hemisphere so that the Northern Hemisphere should warm up first and faster. In fact two third of the greenhouse enhanced with the Northern Hemisphere shows virtually no trend in its temperatures over the last fifty years. There are some very warm readings at the end of the record. I would submit, however, that they are not of the magnitude that one would expect if we were around either the medium or the high temperature scenario.

The sea surface temperature record of Newell *et al* has some very interesting features which I would like to point out to you. It rises from about 1900 to about 1940, undergoes a slow and time decline through the 1960/1970 period and rises again. The correlation between this and an only slightly time increase, land temperature is very high, giving rise to the argument that ocean temperature lag may, in fact, not be all that long. That is one interpretation of this. There is another interpretation that is deep ocean processes are holding back the warming for a very long time. To tell the truth, no-one knows what the answer is. If we assume that the globe's temperature rise of the last one hundred years is primarily because of human greenhouse, then for a doubling of CO_2 the rise would be about 1.3°C. If we assume that very little of it is from the human greenhouse, then the oceanic thermal lag is very, very long because it has already gone over half way to an effective doubling of carbon dioxide.

If you take a least squares trendline into the global temperature curve of Jones and Wigley beginning in 1885, estimated through 1925, 1930, 1935 etc, what you see is approximately 90% of the warming occurred before most of the trade gas forcing increase in the atmosphere.

Additionally, if you look at global carbon emissions, essentially the globe's industrial activity and correlate it into temperatures you find that just as the greenhouse forcing increased dramatically something stopped the warming that was occurring.

If the political debate were rational on this issue, this factor alone should be sufficient to defeat any expensive policy initiative.

Consider the US national temperatures from 1890 to 1989. There are obviously no trends in this record, it is only 2% of the globe and it happens to be a very good record. One of the most interesting aspects of this record though is the period from 1955 through about 1970 in which the inter-annual variability was very low. In the United States, you can read in the newspapers, the weather should become more variable and it is a result of the greenhouse effect. I submit to you that we have returned to the variability which has characterised the Twentieth Century.

There are other ways to measure the temperature – you can measure the temperature obviously by measuring the pressure and the volume and I have done that over the United States using weather balloons back to 1948 and a surrogate seems to work very well for the mean atmospheric height. This record has no cities in it whatsoever. There is no urban error in barometric pressure reading. It shows a rise of about 1.5°, followed by a fall of about 0.8°C, then another rise.

When this was first submitted for publication, I got a letter back from the editor of the only journal in the United States which is devoted to climate change, saying that the paper would be held to a higher standard of review. Three and a half years later it appeared. What this suggests to me is that maybe the natural variability of regional climate after we take out the urban effect, the confounding effect of thermometers may, in fact, not be different from what we may be projecting for the future.

There is an additional bias in the thermometric records which nobody likes to tell you about. Almost all the long term climate records that are used originated at points of commerce, which means that they are usually in river valleys. River valleys are where cold air pools at night and that may very well mask the true variability that exists in the temperature records. When we get into the free atmosphere we start seeing things like this.

Here is the interesting question – are we doing something that is, in fact, mitigating the warming and would that continue?

If we are putting sulphates in the atmosphere that are enhancing the brightness of clouds which can also change the amount I might add, we should observe the following five things:

1. Enhanced night time warming. We should see some enhanced night time warming from the greenhouse, particularly over the areas where there is not a great deal of advection such as in polar night, such as in the middle of continents where the wind is not blowing at night. The temperature decline rate at night should be slowing down. If the clouds are increasing that should in fact be enhanced. At the same time for having the increase in clouds, the day time temperature should not show the same increase. In other words, there should be an effect on the daily energy balance when the daily temperature range would start to decline. We should expect to see these effects concentrated in the Northern Hemisphere because the resident time of sulphate is in the order of weeks or months (carbon dioxide many, many decades if not a century or so), and enhanced brightening of low level cloud should be observed near the ostensible source regions.

Another interesting case is that of summer maximum temperatures in the United States. (These are day time high temperatures in the warmest part of the year.) After 1950, they all fall below the trendline established before that year. While the night time temperatures continue to rise. Why is this important? Because a night time warming destroys most of the apocalypse. You see, the apocalytic scenarios; a crop-yield loss, forest migration etc are driven by the things that effect plants. What kills plants, as surely as we all die of lack of oxygen, is lack of water and that is primarily heightened during the day when the evaporation rate goes up. Projections of increased drought are projected assuming that warming is partitioned equally into the day and the night. If it is partitioned primarily to the night, that does not occur.

The last two decades do in fact show some ostensible increases in rain fall and it has been relatively moist. That is suggestive, in fact, that maybe the cloud effect was beginning to kick in.

The best ground-based rate climate record on the planet, is Tom Karl's historical climate network. A diligent effort was made to remove all the city effects from this record. It shows that daily high temperatures across the continental US rise at the beginning of the record to about 1930 or 1935 and then they start to undergo a slow but unsteady decline. It shocks most people who are enamoured of the popular vision, and there are many of them in North America, when they see the daily high temperatures are running near their lowest value for the Twentieth Century.

Daily low temperatures rise to about 1930, then they start to decline and then they begin to rise. This is the difference between the daily high and the low temperature. When we get to about 1950, the daily range begin to rocket on down. This is a change that has nothing to do with the fact that this is a small percentage of the earth. This change has to do with the daily energy balance, and what it is saying is that mean daily temperature ranges are now averaging near two standard deviations below their mean for the Twentieth Century.

With the IPCC one of the things I wanted to be done, that was not, was to take (in the temperature trends section) the high and low temperature records that existed and to show the change to the daily range that was occurring. What happens when you do that and, from the IPCC data with the United States, you can see the daily range declining. It is the same with mainland China. Go to the Southern Hemisphere, in Australia, you do not see a change. In fact, in virtually every record you look for this in the Northern Hemisphere you see it. In virtually every record in the Southern Hemisphere you do not see the change in the Southern Hemisphere. Clearly, there is a difference between the Hemispheres that is occurring right now with respect to daily energy values.

Ice core records have been referrred to, well look at some other things on the ice core records like the record of sulphate from the Greenland ice core of Mayewski *et al*. The standing crop of sulphates in the atmosphere now is equal to the maximum from Tambora which is credited with reducing again the surface temperature of the globe by 2 degrees celsius for a short period of time. If the oceanic thermal lag were short, given the trace gas change that we have, the atmosphere should have warmed up $2\frac{1}{2}°C$. Is it in fact true that the sulphate effect could be as much as 2°C. 2½ minus 2 equals ½ and that is observed warming of the Twentieth Century. Is it all that simple?

Finally, take a transect across the ocean. We are going to go from the sulphate source region of the United States and transect to approximately Portugal and measure the cloud albedo or reflectivity of the ocean surface strato cumulus. The energy balance equation tells us very subtle changes, slight changes in global reflectivity compensate for the emissivity changes that occur with an increase of carbon dioxide. I would like to point out that the albedo reflectivity on this transect declines by about 7% or 8%.

The Eurasian industrial plume shows again, a decline of about 7% or 8%. When the normal scientific process intercepted this data it was suggested that maybe this was a result of particulates and dust blowing off the continent having a similar effect. A control study was done taking a transect off Australia. Australia is a nice dusty continent, the only thing it does not have that North America or Eurasia have are people and industry. It showed no change.

Is this in fact a literally smoking gun that explains the reluctance of the globe to get with the apocolyptic warming programme? Is the amount of negative forcing as great as Tambora which is demonstrated in the Greenland ice cap? These are certainly things that we must think about as we embrace the so-called high road policy.

Northern Hemisphere cloudiness from millions of ship board observations increases by about 3%. We do not see as much of an increase in the Southern Hemisphere record, although we do see some.

Finally, what have we observed under the hypothesis? We have observed enhanced night warming from increased greenhouse and increased clouds, a counteraction of the day time warming from greenhouse forcing because of the increase in clouds. We have observed a decrease in the daily temperature range, the effect seems to be concentrated primarily in the Northern Hemisphere and we have observed enhanced brightening near the sulphate source region. This allows us to continue to entertain the hypothesis.

I will now proceed to make a forecast.

Since the mid-1980's, climate models have tended to reduce the estimates of warming for doubling carbon dioxide by adding improved oceanic atmosphere interactions. There were twelves and sixteens, there are now fours, sixes and eights, but there is still an awful lot of warming there in the high latitudes which should give you cause for concern.

So you see there are areas of concern. I would be concerned too if the earth were flat, but I am a little bit less concerned because the earth is round. Those projections, and we see them in the newspapers, in the news magazines, everywhere, are massive distortions of the amount of warming.

So what we have is a convergence that we would expect in science between models and reality.

I think what we are seeing here, as the models become more sophisticated, is in fact some reduction in the forecast. Think about weather forecasting: one of the things that I teach my classes is when the tendency of the models is to begin to drop the amount of forecast product out, think about snow. When the model initially forecast a half a metre of snow and the next time it runs the forecast to a quarter of a metre of snow, what we usually get is not a quarter, usually the tendency is for the decline to continue as the models begin to catch up with reality. That may be what we are seeing here.

QUESTIONS

(1) QUESTION: David Fester
                          Environmental Resources Ltd

Clearly, Professor Michaels, you do not see any reason for action now, or at least action on the scale that has been talked about. Do you see no reason or action at all on the greenhouse effect, or are there risk minimising policies you do feel would be warranted?

ANSWER: Professor Michaels

My fear frankly is that if we base I think reasonable imprudent energy policies, meaning energy efficiencies – I do not think anyone is going to argue against energy efficiency – If we base them on global warming as the centre-piece of the policy, and I have read an awful lot of publications that say that global warming is the most important environmental issue, if the issue begins to diffuse do we not lose the basis for an otherwise rational and reasonable policy? I am suggesting that we ought to be very careful about basing our policy on this issue.

(2) QUESTION: Michael Grab
Royal Institute of International Affairs, London

Given the amount of natural variability in climate, which we all understand and recognise, I was really quite startled at what seemed to be the strength of observational evidence that you presented in broadly supporting the idea that sulphates or other factors associated with industrial activity are increasing cloud cover and in other ways tending to off-set heat retention from the greenhouse effect reflectable in terms of the night time warming and other evidence you suggested.

What interests me is what follows from that in the way of policy implications. I think it is a fairly broad acceptance that sulphate levels have reached beyond really acceptable levels in Europe and they are being brought down fairly rapidly. I think it is fairly clear that one could not see the kind of expansions in coal use projected worldwide, without some form of sulphur clean-up.

Does that mean that as efforts are made to increase sulphur and other sorts of pollution that one would expect to be seeing a very strong temperature rise as more of a natural greenhouse effect comes through, or more generally what are the implications? It seems to me that what we are saying is that there are actually several ways in which we are potentially interfering with climate. We are not quite sure what the relative importances are, and that does not really make me any more comfortable about the idea of continuing to increase the rate at which one is changing the atmosphere in various ways on the off-chance that they will cancel in terms of overall climate. It seems to me equally arguable that there would be other side effects, other sorts of climate variations, not perhaps directly associated with temperature rises.

I wondered if you could address that and perhaps clarify quite how much weighting you are putting on the sulphur issue because you seem to be putting quite a lot at one stage in your talk.

ANSWER: Professor Michaels

You will note that several arguments have been made in literature suggesting exactly what you have said, namely that now if you were to drastically curtail, for example, the burning of coal that you would induce the 'heat pulse' – I believe those are the words that Hanson used in his article – in the atmosphere. That very well may be true, but I would also like to point out, not recommending a policy, that it appears that human beings in fact do have other tools at their disposal that may not in fact be nearly as disruptive as a 60% to 80% reduction in carbon emission.

I do not think that the numbers are out on this in any form and it is hard for me not to look at the behaviour and not say that we ought to investigate this problem a lot more. I realise that is not the answer that you want, but nobody has a hard answer.

ANSWER: Dr Houghton

If I may just comment on that and it is an interesting idea. I would like to be the sceptic in this particular regard because I do not think the evidence and the evidence Professor Michaels showed is at all convincing either that there is a large effect from sulphates or, indeed, the cloud cover has changed over the last few decades. Cloud cover is extraordinarily difficult to measure. It is measured by people on ships who estimate cloud cover and so on. It is very hard to be consistent, much harder to be consistent about that than almost any other measurement that we make, and it is only as we get satellite measurements that we can hope to have a consistent record of cloud cover from which to get any real evidence as to whether the cloud cover is changing or not. I remain very sceptical about the effect of sulphates on climate, although it is a very interesting idea to pursue, and I recognise there are some measurements on clouds which do show on the eastern seaboard of continents that albedos are a bit higher.

The second thing is that I would also be very worried about the argument that perhaps we are seeing some balancing here. The idea that you can balance one environmental problem with another and that we are clever enough to know how to do it, or even to direct it in some broad manner, I think is extraordinarily dangerous, particularly when both are subject to uncertainty and, in particular, the sulphate is subject to a great deal of speculation and uncertainty. I believe that is really a very dangerous argument to use and one we should avoid. We cannot manipulate the climate advertently at all easily, and we should be very wary arguing that we can.

ANSWER: Professor Michaels

First of all, human beings have been modifying their climate for a long time. As an example, the climate of Washington DC in the 1950's was colder in the winter than the climate of Charlottesville, one hundred miles south, it is now warmer. Simply by the urban effect, we raise the mean temperature for the region about 1°C.

Secondly, I am not so sure that it is not characteristic of human beings to balance problems with other infusions of unnatural substances, and I call your attention to yourselves that when you are ill you take things that you normally would not take. The result is an equilibrium. Furthermore, there is another very serious argument that must be addressed, which is the intellectual capital argument. It is the use of fossil fuels in the last one hundred years that allowed your life span to go up by about three decades. The mean crop yields increased by a factor of five in North America.

We may be confronted with making the decision do we continue an economic policy that allows the development of that type of intellectual capital which may frankly include much of the current fuel mix, plus some additional ones. Or, do we purposefully limit economic growth as a result of global warming. We are now getting far beyond the realm of climatology, but I would suggest that if I had my choice I would probably chose the former.

(3) QUESTION: Richard Courtney
                 British Association of Colliery
                 Management

I am concerned about the differences between theory and predictions and observations in the real world. I cite, for example, the work of Co Limberg and Thompson, published in Nature last year, where they have compared the climate records both of CO_2 concentration and temperature and discerned that the parameters cohere such that changes in the CO_2 lag behind changes in the temperature by five months. This is precisely the reverse of the greenhouse theory and the model predictions. Can someone explain to me why what one sees happening is exactly the reverse of cause and effect as claimed in the theory?

ANSWER: Dr Houghton

The ice core record is, of course, quite difficult to time and that is one estimate of the phase lag between the two. I think nobody doubts that temperature actually affects CO_2. Why has the CO_2 changed during the ice age periods? It has changed because of changes in the total earth's climate system, including its temperature, and the response of that system which includes biology in the ocean and on the land surface which has been the major reason why that CO_2 has changed.

The greenhouse effect is the reverse of that which is the influence of CO2 in its turn on temperature. Now both of these are occurring. It's very hard to gauge, even from a measurement of phase lag which is hard to make, as to the magnitude of each of those effects. But, as far as the greenhouse effect is concerned, I would just pass you back again to the fact that we live in a world which has a temperature of around 15°C, or thereabouts, and the reason why it is so warm is because of the greenhouse effect. We have 33° or so of that greenhouse effect keeping us warm now. What we are talking about in this instance is the enhanced greenhouse effect due to increase of these greenhouse gases, and what we are arguing about is just how big it is going to be. The greenhouse effect is there, basically keeping us warm, nobody actually doubts that.

ANSWER: Professor Michaels

I would just like to reiterate your question because I think it points out that there are several problems which may be more under the title of why has it not warmed up as much as it should have?

(4) QUESTION: Horst Wiesbach
                  Unido

I have a question relating to the report where you relate to the deforestation, which is very interesting, but has an attempt been made to model the whole question of recycling of CO_2 into bio-mass and that effect, and if it is possible on the energy balance? I think the question is not only theoretical, it could have very practical implications for the whole agricultural and economic policy.

ANSWER: Dr Houghton

Very quickly on deforestation, if you try to do a carbon budget on the world, you find you cannot balance your books. There is a significant carbon sink which we do not know whether it exists on the land biosphere or the ocean biosphere, and the effect of deforestation is estimated, but it is not at all easy to estimate as you can imagine, what is the rate of carbon decay in the bio-mass of a forest. There are some big problems there, and perhaps I should leave it at that.

ANSWER: Professor Michaels

I would just like to point out something that might strike you as interesting in the new climate models which result in the dramatic expansion of the tropical rain forest beyond its current state. I think that we should also observe that there are possible positive interactions between climate change and the ecosphere that I do not think we are paying any attention to.

(5) QUESTION: Sonia Christensen
                  University of Sussex

This is more a comment than a question. I think we appreciate seeing the range of the scientific debate and nobody can deny that the current debate about global warming is wonderful for science and development of models and scientific knowledge. However, I think one of the speakers went a little bit too far when he came here as an advocate of American energy policy. I think the judgements about fossil fuels and economic growth are not scientific judgements and should not really be made by people who present themselves primarily as scientists.

The second thing I wanted to say is, there is a counter strategy to all this because while the scientists may be talking in the anglo saxon world, in other countries it may be the engineers that are running the debate and they may come up with a more energy efficient solution while we keep on talking here about the science. As I said, the emphasis on science is important, I am glad we have started with it, but I noted there are no engineers on the programme. Perhaps we should take the engineers into account.

ANSWER: Professor Michaels

I think the comments are well taken and I appreciate them.

3

WHAT EFFECT MIGHT DEFORESTATION HAVE ON GLOBAL CLIMATE?

Dr Jane Goodall

Director, Jane Goodall Institute

It is not a subject that I am used to addressing as such, long term changes in global climate. I am more used to speaking, as I am sure most of you realise, about chimpanzees in Tanzania. I promise that I will not be speaking about chimpanzees here.

There certainly is evidence from many extremely reputable scientists that the destruction of forests and the use of the top soils for agricultural purposes do tend to increase the build up of carbon dioxide emissions in the world's atmosphere. Not to the same extent as the burning of fossil fuels which we have talked more about during today, but certainly to some extent.

Hundreds and thousands of square miles of forests have already gone. Can preserving the remaining great forests of the world and perhaps, planting new trees, help to alleviate the problem which we face today as a result of having destroyed so much of the green covering of the world?

It seems, from what I have read, that even extraordinarily extensive reforestation programmes can only serve to slow down the greenhouse effect in the world today. If we accept the prediction of many eminent scientists as to the very grave consequences of global changes in climate which seem to be occurring today, then I believe that every little helps and, on the other side of the coin, even if reforestation and preserving forests did not make any difference at all to the greenhouse effect, it would still be extremely worth doing because of the very major benefits, particularly in third world countries, that preserving forests and reforestation can have. I will come back to those presently.

Does the developed world have any responsibility to ensure that various technologies that may have caused part of the environmental problem that we face today are not used to adverse effect in the third world?

Certainly some of the international corporations who make their money not only in the developed world, but by sending out exploration teams, like the oil companies, logging companies, mining companies, all the other industrial companies that move out into the remaining natural forests of the world, must face some kind of responsibility. I believe that it is their responsibility to develop methods of doing whatever it is that they are doing in the forests that make as little environmental impact as possible, on the assumption that these environmental impacts are degrading the world climate.

If we take the logging companies, they can develop selective logging techniques which are a little harder and which cost a little more, but are very definitely less destructive to the forest overall. I am told by foresters, and I have spent some time talking with them, that these techniques while providing them with the necessary timber can, at the same time, help the remaining trees to sustain the natural populations of animals and vegetation in those forests that they are, at the same time, exploiting.

The oil companies can reek total devastation on areas that were virgin forest before they came in. They can do it, to some extent, simply by their seismic drilling operations because some companies will drive straight through the forest where they could actually move around the outskirts. The great danger in these operations lies in the opening up of the forest by means of the roads that the

Global Warming: The Debate
Edited by Peter Thompson with the assistance of John P. O'Hara

companies build in order to take their heavy vehicles to oil wells or to suspected oil wells. The same thing can also be said of mining companies and other such people who move into the forest.

Once a road is made, then the hunters will follow. The local people will start developing on either side of the road, and you can see beautiful pictures from satellites showing that, as a road is driven deep into the forest, so the trees begin to disappear gradually fanning out into what was untouched. Of course, this is devastating for the animal life in the area, as well as losing the trees.

I have been fortunate enough to work with Conoco Oil. I have observed how their seismic drilling explorations make very little impact on the environment at all. Whereas they accept that once oil is found there will be some destruction of the forest in that area, their policy, developed by Roger Simpson who is Head of Exploration in the Congo and who is British, is that even if we must destroy a piece of the forest here, let us have a net gain for the environment. We will use proceeds from the oil companies' money to protect the environment as a whole. One strategy is that the entire concession be changed into a national park, with the proviso that the oil company is allowed to continue to operate within that national park. The great advantage here is that the roads that are built by the oil company instead of being used to cut down the forest in other parts, will be protected: the local people will not be able to use them, but they could be used to develop forest tourism.

I believe that international corporations do have a responsibility in the area of the surviving rain forests and the second question is how do we persuade the governments of developing countries to protect their remaining rain forests?

The third world accept perhaps that some of the results of modern technology are extremely destructive of the environment. They blame the developed world for having increased the greenhouse effect, among other things such as increasing pollutants in the air, but especially the governments want to increase the economic standing of their countries. They want to use the technologies that we have used to destroy large parts of our own environment, and why should they not? I have lived for a long time in Africa and I know what it is like to be in an extraordinarily economically poor country. A rather different sort of country to Eastern Europe which we heard about this morning because, in Africa, as some of you know, poverty really is poverty and people are struggling to get enough to eat.

Is it not right that the governments would seek to use all the skills that western technology has developed in order to improve their own economies and to raise the standards of living of their people, and to hell with the environment?

I think that it is at this point that we must say to ourselves – are we going to stand by and let this happen to the last great forests in the world just because we fully understand why the people in the third world feel that they should have access to all our energy wasting methods? I think instead it behoves us to work even harder to develop alternative methods that will be less costly in the use of energy that will produce less emissions increasing the greenhouse effect, so that we can give an example. We can help the third world to do things to improve their economy not repeating all our mistakes, but rather making use of the fact that we have learned from our mistakes and we are searching for newer and better ways of doing the same things in the future. In other words, I personally feel that the developed world should be prepared now to pay back something of the wealth which we have plundered from the natural world around us.

That is in the long term. What about in the short term? Are there any ways that we can persuade an African or a South American or an Indonesian government to preserve a patch of primary forest which they feel, and rightly, that they could exploit for much needed foreign exchange by selling that forest as a concession to some large timber company, or to an oil company, or anything of that sort. One option, of course, is that we can simply buy the piece of forest and I think it was World Wildlife that pioneered the debt swap for nature with paying back some of our debts to the environment. As I say, we got rich from plundering it. We use some of that money to buy a piece of forest in exchange for the debt in foreign exchange of that particular country. That is a method which has been used and has been used quite effectively in a number of countries.

We can strive to help the government see other ways of gaining foreign exchange from the exploitation of the forest and exploitation that is kinder than logging or searching for oil and some of these other industrial occupations. We can try to develop what I call forest tourism. We can develop forest national parks. We can make it possible for people who are hungry for new kinds of adventures, some people are tired of driving round Savanna country and looking at the animals in Tanzania and Kenya, and would love to go out in the forest if they could see the wonderful animals that lived there. We can make it possible for this to happen and, as I say, develop forest tourism. We can help the people in the country to be proud of what they have. We can give them international pats on the back for conserving some of their heritage. We can train the local people, the hunters, instead of killing the animals that live there and cutting down the trees, to be the proud guardians of large expanses of forest.

We can also help governments to save forest areas by helping the people around the forest. That is extremely important because no forest will be saved simply by a government making strict rules and punishing people for disobeying. People have to make a living and some people have lived by working in the forest hunting or searching for various other forest products. We can employ some of them to guard forest areas, but we can also be helpful by assisting in rural development programmes on the outskirts of these areas that we are trying to save, these large reservoirs of endemic trees. We can assist with healthcare in surrounding areas and, I think personally, that no healthcare programme should be implemented without a parallel family planning programme going on at the same time.

We can help them to develop things like game farming and, most particularly in this context of supreme importance, is agro-forestry. You help people to grow trees as crops. People who for years have made their living in the forest by cutting them down for building poles, for charcoal, for fire wood, for living in their own village and for selling to get some money. They can grow these trees. The growing of trees will help to prevent soil erosion and, in some parts of Africa where I have been, the clear cutting, slash and burn agriculture has led to such horrifying soil erosion, particularly on the edge of Lake Tanganyika where I am most familiar with it. In many places, the forests have completely gone and, with every rain, more and more of the rather thin layer of soil is being washed down into Lake Tanganyika. The planting of trees is helping to prevent soil erosion and it is helping to save valuable water tables.

Typically, when we think of agro-forestry, growing of trees, reforestation, we think of some of the very successful programmes of growing eucalyptus and pine, species that are not endemic but which grow fast, and this can be extremely useful for the reasons I have just stated. It is not particularly useful for wildlife. There are not many creatures in Africa who can make a living in pine and eucalyptus forests because they simply are not adapted for living in and feeding on those species. However, in Burundi, where I have now been working for the past two and half years, they have some extremely innovative agro-forestry programmes which have resulted from intensive research on indigenous tree species and, to my amazement, I have been round some of these areas where they have developed these programmes, and found that some indigenous trees can grow to forty feet or more in just two years which is very fast growth. Forests like this built around the indigenous forests for one extend the habitat of the sometimes very pressurised animal species living within the indigenous forest, but they also act as a barrier to prevent the local people from going further into the natural forests. I believe that agro-forestry programmes are extremely beneficial and we are trying to develop, along with Canadian aid, some extensive reforestation projects right along the shores of Lake Tanganyika from Burundi, up beyond Kigoma.

The people who grow these areas of new forests can practice their age old traditions in forests that they have grown themselves. They can continue to cut trees for building poles. They can continue to collect firewood. They can make charcoal and, to some extent, they can export these products and so increase the income of members of their family. In addition, just within the last few years, among the people of Tanzanier that I am most familiar with and in Burundi, these local people, the farmers, the villagers, are actually beginning to understand the relationship between the indiscriminate clear cutting of trees for agriculture and the soil erosion and the lack of rain. Around where I am working in Tanzania, individuals in their own farms have actually begun planting trees. They themselves on their own initiate. There are a number of small programmes developing where little tiny nurseries are being started and seedlings are being grown and, in some cases, school children are being responsible for planting those seedlings and nurturing them into growth.

I think there is great hope in this sphere. It just needs a little gentle encouragement from the rest of the world and, as I say, a few little pats on the back. We tend to forget so often that these people in some of these developing countries and I speak of Africa and East Africa, where I know the people the best, they are very proud. If they can be made to feel proud of something they have done, whether it is for their own good, or for the good of the global environment, then that is a great incentive to them to continue to do it. Of course, they need some economic incentive as well, we all do. They have to live just as we do.

Finally, of course, we have to be concerned with education. At this point we can leave Africa and we can think about educating children in problems of this sort around the world. There is a great hunger for information among many of the people I have spoken with, and we are not just speaking about the developing world but also the industrialised nations. Children read an awful lot in the media, but very often it is not brought down to a level where they feel that they can be helpful. There are some programmes in Europe, in America, as well as in Africa where children are personally responsible for planting trees. I think that these sorts of programmes, combined with an understanding of the sort of effects that can happen if all trees are cut down are extremely beneficial.

I am not a scientist with respect to deforestation and the effects which this might have on global warming, but I do know from talking to people in West Africa, for example, people who have lived there for many years, that when they first went there thirty years ago there were two rainy seasons in many parts of West Africa. At first, the local people,

the farmers were saying 'the short rains are very late this year'. They do not say that any more because the short rains no longer occur. There is just one rainy season and what the farmers are saying now is 'the rains are late' – not the long rains or the short rains, but the rains because we are reduced to one rainy season as the desertification effects of deforestation are increased.

Let me sum up then by saying that I believe that preserving our remaining forests and planting trees wherever we can and growing them is a desperately important undertaking for both the developed and the developing world. Even if the cutting down of trees, deforestation, has no effect on global warming, even so the benefit of looking after our remaining forests is tremendous. The benefits of planting new forests in areas that are being denuded are immense and can make for a very great increase in the standard of living and the comfort of daily life for thousands of people, for their livestock, and can actually prevent the extinction, at least in the short term, of thousands of animal species.

Let us face it, even if the most gloomy scientists are proved right, even if we have progressed so far along the path to the destruction of the natural world that we, as a species, along with the other creatures of the world, are doomed. Even if that is true, it is not going to happen for a while and we owe it to future generations, as many as there are, to preserve an environment that is the best we can possibly leave for them. Even a condemned man is given his last breakfast.

QUESTIONS

(1) QUESTION: Professor Michaels

One of the things that interests me is the tenor of your talk. You are a strong believer in the need to preserve and expand, if possible, tropical forests. What would you do if there was a climate model, a very sophisticated one, that when coupled to a vegetation model said if the CO_2 concentration of the atmosphere increases over the next fifty years then the tropical forest would expand dramatically? Those two models actually exist: the Q-flux model and Hank Schugert's vegetation model.

ANSWER: Dr Jane Goodall

I am delighted. Does that model take into account everything? Is it taking into account the relatively new environmental movements to preserve the forest?

QUESTION: Professor Michaels

This model, in fact, starts in the Indian Sub-Continent. It starts with essentially the bare ground and the very sparse cover that we have today. Left to run on its own accord, because of the way the warming distributes itself seasonally, the entire Sub-Continent blooms into tropical rain forests by somewhere towards the end of the next century.

ANSWER:

I am absolutely overjoyed is all I can say. You must tell me where I can read it.

QUESTION:

I am merely reporting the news, not commenting on it. You might want to contact the US Environmental Protection Agency.

(2) QUESTION: Neil Furman
                  Intramark, United States

What has impressed me about Dr Goodall's talk is not so much about one incidence in a particular forest, but that this is all part of a much broader environmental issue that we all need to face. The global warming is just one part of it. The fact that a particular CO_2 model works in Africa really, in the scheme of things, is not important. What we need to focus on is a really serious and sincere environmental focus in the world of which global warming is just one part. Dr Goodall I thank you for your human contribution to the debate and getting down to the basics of what needs to be done, getting out of the armchair, corporate attorney style viewpoint of these issues and down to what really needs to be done.

(3) QUESTION: Adam Markham
                  Worldwide Fund for Nature

I just wanted to come back to the model on tropical forests. I also have not seen that model, but I presume that it cannot take into account the ecological dynamics of actually developing a tropical forest because the problem is that we have been trying, or foresters have been trying, for years to re-establish natural tropical forests and have virtually completely failed. As far as I know, there is no existing re-establishment in an already climatically acceptable area of natural forests. That it putting aside the land use pressures of the graded soils and of people coming into the area, chopping down the seedlings etc. It is all very well to have a nice model which says 'the climatic conditions would be OK', but we have to take into account the fact that our forestry skills do not go that far yet.

My second point is that I felt I ought to mention the idea of debt swaps which Dr Goodall discussed. It is important to point out that the debt swaps that we have been involved in so far have not actually involved buying land. What we have tried to do is to buy small amounts of debt on the secondary market and then put that debt back into control of the governments, but on the understanding that through a strong local non-governmental organisation that money will be used specifically for designated conservation purposes. There has been a little bit of misunderstanding about the idea of northern groups coming into developing countries and buying land because, obviously, people in developing countries find that a sort of colonialist attitude. That is not the way that we have been approaching it.

(4) QUESTION: Mr Evans
                  Weston Riding, Australia

I would just like to pick up the previous comment in relation to rain forests. Experience is that you do not need any forestry skills to grow rain forests, the problem is to stop them growing particularly in the sugar cane areas of North Queensland. It is a constant battle to keep the sugar cane and the rain forests out of your property.

(5) QUESTION: Nicola Steen
                Royal Institute of International
                Affairs

We are not looking at the forests in isolation obviously and, like Dr Goodall said, she is concerned
about the people who live in the area. Surely, the
issue we are concerned about today is global warming and, to make comments such as CO_2 rise might
help global conditions for reforestation, this does
not take into consideration the concerns of people
who also would be affected, or could be affected,
by climate change such as sea level rise: people
who live in Egypt, for example. It is very misleading to make comments that would look just at reforestation and say 'therefore, that is good'. As we
keep saying, all these topics are tied up together
and there could be very negative aspects that we
need to be concerned with as well.

ANSWER: Dr Jane Goodall

I think that is a good point and also somebody
can correct me if I am wrong, but I read that one
aspect of the fertilisation of plants by increased
levels of CO2 is that there tends to be less protein
and more carbohydrate in the leaves, and the
leaves tend to get larger as a result. The insect
pests have great problems when this happens because there is not enough protein, they eat more
of the leaf, and one meal is more bites for the
insect because he is trying to get the protein. The
response of the plant to that is to grow bigger
leaves which are less and less nourishing for the
people eating them.

(6) QUESTION: Richard Courtney,
                British Association of Colliery
                Management

Dr Goodall, like you, I share great concern for
the rain forests and I think it is imperative that
we protect them and expand them if only to protect the genome stock.
    Two speakers have tried to link rain forest pro-
tection and expansion to a macro set of global
environmental issues, notably global warming

which confronts us. I think that is extremely dangerous. If global warming, with all its uncertainties,
comes off the rails as could very easily happen, after
all there is no evidence for it. If it were to come off
the rails and if we tied deforestation to that, we could
pull down interest in the rain forests, along with the
global warming collapse. I would wish the issue to
be kept separate.

(7) QUESTION: Mr Cooper-Reade
                Eastern Electricity

I was interested in your comment, Dr Goodall,
about large companies buying part of the rain
forest to preserve it. It strikes me that there is a
major opportunity there to exploit perhaps the
attitude in this country and for some companies
to pick up on the green issue and promotions
which enable the customer to buy part of the rain
forest would perhaps do a lot more good than just
one large company buying it. Do you not think
you could exploit this commercialisation in some
way?

ANSWER : Dr Jane Goodall

I am glad that you said that actually because this
is not what I meant. I must have been unclear.
What Conoco has actually done is to persuade the
government to create the National Park. My involvement is to try and develop alternative methods
of livelihood for the people who previously have
lived in the forest by hunting, as well as to help
the government create the National Park which
will be government property and which, one hopes
will produce tourist revenue. It is the creation of
the National Park by the government that will keep
out hunters and loggers and prevent people from
using these roads.

(8) QUESTION : Peter Bright
                 Shell International

I just add that, in the international oil industry, we
are sharing our experiences in this area and developing guidelines that can be used by the industry generally.

(9) QUESTION :   Adam Markham,
                  World Wide Fund for Nature

I would just like to come back to the issue of taking the forestry question away from the rest of the climate debate. I am quite surprised to hear people say that they think the climate debate will suddenly disappear and evaporate. I think it would be foolish to think that and I think the climate debate is going to get stronger. It is going to be linked much more with the energy question, as people are talking about 'no regrets' policies, that we are going to have to do something about out energy consumption if people in developing countries are to come anywhere near our present standard of living.

The question of taking the forestry issue away from the rest of the climate debate is quite crucial because of the position of the United States in the negotiations. The forestry issue is a soft option. You can be under public pressure to do something about forestry and you can go forward internationally, if you separate forestry from energy.

The United States wants to separate forestry from energy because, in their political terms, it is necessary to make that separation because the developing countries will say 'we are not going to do anything about preserving our forests, if you do not do anything to reduce your energy consumption'. For countries which have a high per capita energy consumption, and they are under public pressure to do something about forestry, it is important for them to make that separation in the debate. It is important, if we want to reduce per capita consumption in the northern countries, that we do not make that separation, that we do not marginalise the developing countries' problems of forestry and put it into a separate forum.

Part II

The Energy Debate

4

THE CONTINUING NEED FOR ENERGY AND ALTERNATIVE ENERGY SOURCES

Helga Steeg

Executive Director, International Energy Agency

If we look at statements by environmental organisations, political parties and also by members of governments on the future energy path in the light of environmental concerns, the picture is often very confusing. People see a huge potential for energy conservation, they want no nuclear power plants, no hydroelectric plants and, as far as possible, no large technical facilities whatsoever. They are against oil and gas exploration projects and the transport of oil and gas, and ask for a sharp reduction in coal used because of the high CO_2 emissions.

At the same time, they expect no change, most of them at any rate, or even an improvement in the present living standards, greater comfort, greater mobility, economic growth and price stability, and massive aid for economic progress in developing countries and other regions of the world such as, in particular, Central and Eastern Europe. All in all, Mr Chairman, I believe an array of demands that are not easy to reconcile.

In order to bring some rationalism into the debate, the IEA is analysing on a periodic basis the long term outlook for world energy demand and supply, under a number of different assumptions about crude oil prices, economic growth and a host of other variables.

Forecasting future energy developments over a longer period is always fraught with considerable uncertainty, particularly in the present situation where the political situation in the Gulf crisis after the war is far from having been stabilised, but also rapid and unforeseeable economic changes in Eastern Europe and the Soviet Union contribute to an increase in uncertainty regarding the future. There-

fore, our outlook is intended to be only indicative of the direction and possible evolution of worldwide energy trends.

Let us look at a scenario which assumes that oil prices settle after the Gulf war at twenty three dollars per barrel in real terms, and then gradually rise to thirty-five by early in the next decade and remain at this level thereafter and, I repeat, this is an assumption on the scenario – we all watch what the oil prices have been doing and it remains to be seen where they will go during the course of this year. At any rate, on the assumption of this scenario, we expect that the total world energy demand will rise at an average annual rate of 2.4% over the next fifteen years.

The increase in the OECD region will be much lower, with an annual rate of 1.2%. However, in developing countries, we expect a 4.2% yearly increase and in Central Eastern Europe and the Soviet Union an above average rate of 2.3% can be expected. In total, these numbers mean that, in the period from 1989 up to the year 2005, world energy demand is expected to grow by almost 45% and even OECD energy demand is expected to grow by more than 20%. If we translate this into CO_2 emissions using commonly agreed emission factors for the different fuels, we arrive at almost the same percentage numbers.

The CO_2 growth rate might be slightly lower than the energy growth rate since we expect certain shifts towards less CO_2 emitting energies. It has to be pointed out in this context that our outlook presents what we call a 'business as usual' scenario which means that in each case we assume a continuation of current energy policies.

Global Warming: The Debate
Edited by Peter Thompson with the assistance of John P. O'Hara

Many governments are presently contemplating far reaching changes in their energy policy, particularly with regard to the issue of global climate change. Some of these changes, if adopted, could have profound impact on energy consumption and, therefore, also on the result on our energy outlook. Nevertheless, the figures I mention show the background against which we have to assess the effort of OECD countries to establish targets for the stabilisation or reduction of greenhouse gases and, in particular, CO_2 emissions.

Almost all IEA countries (and we had yesterday invited Finland to join us and we will invite France to join us, so now, with the exception of Iceland, it is identical to the OECD countries) have, in the past few months, developed policies which aim at limiting energy related CO_2 emissions. In most cases, these goals so far are conditional and they are not yet decisions on concrete policies and plans for action. Our energy outlook shows how far away we are still from the CO_2 emission stabilisation or reduction targets which are presently being discussed, as you know, both nationally and internationally.

The outlook also shows how important it is to ensure that future energy demand is met by sufficient and secure energy supplies. This is particularly true if we look at the problem from a worldwide perspective. Even if OECD countries would be able to achieve stabilisation and reduction targets, the worldwide effect would be rather limited since we cannot expect similar efforts in Eastern Europe and, in particular, the developing countries where the priorities are different and economic development and growth is their primary policy.

In the last year, many governments and private organisations came up with new plans for revised policies for promoting improvement in energy efficiency and we welcomed this. This greater stress on the demand side initiatives has been caused by environmental concern, but also by difficulties in balancing supply and demand for electricity, in some countries, and more recently by the renewed concerns about the energy situation in the light of the crisis in the Middle East.

Very often, the impression is given that by new emphasis on energy conservation and efficiency, many, if not all, supply and environmental problems

can be solved without major disruptions. I do not want to deny at all that there is still a significant potential for energy efficiency improvements which would lead us beyond the 1.3% decline in energy intensity per year which we have assumed in our energy outlook. We certainly must do better in identifying sector by sector the existing potential, the barriers which prevent this potential from being realised, and the instruments which could be used to overcome the barriers. However, analysis in this respect carried out so far also shows the limitations of energy efficiency improvements.

In the period between 1973 and 1988, the energy intensity of IEA countries declined on average by 1.8% a year. This was achieved as the result of two oil crises and hard economic recessions between 1979 and 1982. It was also the efficiency gain facilitated by the fact that in the 1970's, when major conservation efforts first began, there was a large number of very cost effective measures available which could be easily implemented and had relatively far reaching effects. Therefore, to believe that in the future we could achieve efficiency improvements which go beyond the improvements in the 1970s, would be very optimistic.

Very often, the real market potential for efficiency measures is much smaller than originally expected. Not all of the instruments to enhance energy conservation are as effective as their promoters or makers believe. Many of them could have negative effects on the economy which must be carefully analysed. General statements on the conservation potential that still exists and the possibilities of using it cannot be made because of the varying conditions in the different sectors and countries and the great numbers of producers and consumers involved. Only detailed analysis sector by sector can provide further information.

We in the IEA are working on this kind of analysis. We have recently published a study on electricity end use efficiency and, at present, are analysing other sectors such as, for instance, the very important transport sector.

Let me again stress that there is no such thing as a symmetry between identifying the potential and then believing that the potential can be easily or readily achieved. The multitude of consumers must be taken into account and also, of course, the general economic conditions. Nevertheless, energy efficiency and conservation is, and will be, an important objective both in terms of energy security and environmental protection.

Coming now to the energy sources which we will have to make available to meet future energy needs, I think it becomes apparent from our energy outlook that we cannot do without any of the sources of supply which are presently existing. All energy sources will be necessary for the foreseeable future, although the proportions of these fuels and the fuel mix, in different countries, will certainly be different.

There is much enthusiasm, not only in environmental organisations but also in energy circles, about the future role of renewable sources of energy and, indeed, all efforts should be made to promote these energies. However, the contributions by renewable energy sources to OECD energy supplies, at present amount to only 7% and there is not much perspective that these energies will be in a position to replace a major share of fossil fuels over the next few decades.

Most of the share of renewables comes from hydropower, the potential of which in OECD countries is already widely exploited and which by the way also increasingly meets environmental oppositions. Most other forms of renewables are presently only competitive in special locations and their economies depend on special conditions.

I do not want to belittle the potential importance of these energies and the need to support their development, for instance, by major research and development efforts. However, it is also apparent that at the present stage of development, investment decisions cannot be based on the assumption that renewable energies will be available in sufficient quantities and at competitive costs.

It is often argued that, if the price of what I called the traditional sources – the hydrocarbons, for instance – for electricity would be increased more potential of renewables could be brought to the market. A note of caution because, if you try to redirect the balance of resources, you get into the area of re-allocation of energy sources and you have to very carefully evaluate the impact on the economy as a whole.

Secondly, if one lets off the hook those who work on the reduction of the economic costs of renewables, then you lose completely the encouragement and incentive and you might be faced with the fact that the renewables will almost never become competitive. However, let me again stress both the further development of the technology side and the economic side of renewables is and will remain an important objective in our energy and environmental policy.

There is also a widespread belief that natural gas, with its relatively low carbon content, will provide the cure-all for climate change related problems. However, if natural gas is really going to play a major role in climate change policies of many countries, it must be available at sufficient quantities. With new developments in Norway and Australia, the gas supply situation today looks much more positive than a couple of years ago. New technical developments are opening up further possibilities for gas use, particularly for electricity production, but possibly also in other sectors such as the transport sector.

However, in the light of many projects for additional gas use, the gas supply situation needs continuous monitoring. New large investments in infrastructure which are required to make the gas available to the market and the more demand for gas increases, the high the prices of course will go.

Let us deal with oil for a moment. Ladies and gentlemen, oil will continue to be the most important energy source mainly because of further increase in demand in the transport sector, where practical alternatives are not yet in sight. However, the oil intensity of most economies will decline and, according to new projections, the share of oil in world primary energy requirements will decrease in the period from 1989 to the year 2005 from around 39% to 35%. The Gulf crisis has demonstrated once more how vulnerable our own oil supplies are. Continued efforts, therefore, have to be made to reduce this vulnerability not only by what we have just gone through, the emergency preparedness of IEA countries, but also by the continuing process of substituting other forms of energy for oil.

It was mentioned that the supply of oil is constantly declining. I would like to take some issue with that. There is, for the time being, a very comfortable supply situation in terms of oil without the Kuwait and Iraq oil having come to the market, or will come to the market in the traditional share and very quickly.

Nevertheless, if one looks to the end of the decade and beyond, there is need for further investment in oil and, of course, in other energy sources. The fact that the OECD countries got through this energy crisis and the war situation, without any disruption, is due to the fact that the producing countries who are not called Iraq and Kuwait surged their production capacity way beyond everybody's expectation which shows the flexibility in the system and that our own OECD countries were able also to use more flexibility because there is more efficiency in the energy sector.

Looking to the past, we see that the main shifts in the substitution process away from oil have been made towards nuclear and coal. All IEA countries agree that these shifts have significantly increased our security of supply as was again demonstrated during the last months. There is also agreement between member countries that for the IEA as a whole these two forms of energy will have to play an important role in the future as well. Unfortunately, both energies, coal and nuclear, are facing serious environment concerns.

To make both fuels environmentally acceptable is a challenging goal which requires continued efforts of governments and industry. As far as nuclear is concerned, it is essential that all safety and waste disposal problems related to the nuclear fuel cycle be given maximum attention. The necessity of meeting the highest safety standards is a condition for the operation of nuclear plants worldwide. As public acceptance of nuclear power is critical to the continuation of nuclear programmes, major effort must be made to enhance public participation in decision making, by providing balanced and clear information.

If, by such means, a more positive political climate regarding nuclear is achieved, this energy source could make significant contributions both to energy security and to the environment, given that nuclear power does not produce greenhouse gases or other pollutants associated with fossil fuels.

As far as coal is concerned, the ongoing debate concerning possible climate change could seriously affect future investment decisions for coal projects and developments of coal demand. This could create a real conflict between environmental goals and the goal of energy security for which coal is essential, since it is available in abundance at low cost and from a great variety of suppliers.

As economic technology to remove and dispose of the emitted CO_2 so far do not exist, the only feasible way of reducing CO_2 emissions from coal burning is to increase the efficiency of coal use. Many technologies are already available or are being developed which could help in reaching this goal. The much more efficient coal combustion technologies that are just now reaching the market must succeed and it is crucial that countries in Central and Eastern Europe, and the third world, have access to this technology, especially for those which are major high growth rate coal consumers.

Let me sum up the overview of how we see the energy future:

(1) Due to a number of factors such as economic growth, increasing industrialisation and growing populations, with particular relevance for developing countries, our energy outlook expects significant growth in energy consumption over the next fifteen years. This will be reflected in a slightly smaller but also significant growth in greenhouse gas emissions.

(2) Our outlook does not take into account major changes in energy policies which are being considered in many countries in light of the environmental debate. Such policies could lead to a significant change in future energy demand. However, the analysis on how much can be achieved in this respect, without serious macro economic consequences, is not yet completed. We and the OECD are still working on this.

(3) Given the future needs for energy, we will for the foreseeable time have to rely on all energy sources which are presently being used. All efforts must be made to make these fuels environmentally more acceptable. At the same time, we must promote the research and development on renewable

sources of energy and must begin preparing now for the secure economic and environmental benign energy systems for the future.

(4) Because of the magnitude of the climate change problem, national efforts in themselves are not sufficient. Internationally harmonised efforts are necessary to make sure that the most cost effective and efficient solutions are found and new distortions, such as negative trade effects, are avoided. It seems to me that not enough attention has been given to this, but anybody who follows the almost collapse of the Uruguay round on agriculture, should bear in mind that, if countries erect new trade barriers, we will be in deep trouble in international co-operation and economic growth for the future.

The opening of new markets, for instance in Eastern Europe and the Soviet Union, offer huge opportunities for international co-operation. With the high potential for energy efficiency improvements in these countries, for additional environmental control in these countries, there is a chance for much progress at comparatively low cost. Let us hope that the political developments will allow to realise this potential.

(5) There is also a vital need for the involvement of energy industries in this whole process and I do think the energy industry has a number of possibilities for their contributions:

(a) The development and the application of new technologies.

(b) The use of energy and the production of energy in more efficient ways.

I agree that voluntary codes of conduct cannot be the only way out, but I come from a country which is Germany where we have made very good experience with voluntary codes of industries. I am not saying that one can live without regulation, but the more effective those voluntary codes would be the less strict the government regulations must be.

My last point is that we, the IEA countries, will have a meeting of our Ministers on 3rd June. We just started yesterday to discuss how we are going to prepare it. There will be three major items on the agenda. The first item of course, will be what lessons have we learned in terms of oil policy, energy security from the Gulf crisis. The second will be how are we going to co-operate much more intensively with the non-OECD countries in energy with regard to Central and Eastern Europe and the developing countries. The third item on the agenda will be the integration of energy and environmental problems.

5

INTERNATIONAL COLLABORATION IN CARBON DIOXIDE COLLECTION AND DISPOSAL

Professor John T. McMullan

Director, Centre for Energy Research, University of Ulster

CO_2 Options

What are the various measures that we can take? Fundamentally, the only way of reducing CO_2 in the release to the atmosphere, is to burn less. Therefore, everything boils down to burning less. Anything we can do which means that we burn less fossil fuel, is going to contribute to the reduction of CO_2.

Energy Conservation

We can use energy conservation to reduce the demand for energy. There is still an enormous capacity for energy conservation, but the basic difficulty is that it requires the co-ordinated efforts of a very large number of individuals. We know how difficult that is to achieve. Look at the wonderful effects the anti-smoking campaigns have, or anti-drug abuse campaigns have.

You are asking a large number of individuals, whether they are individual companies or individual people, to always switch off the lights. Switching off lights campaigns last all of three weeks.

Increased Use of Nuclear Power

This is an obvious candidate. Are we going to be allowed to do it? Do we actually want to do it? I will leave that to a later speaker.

Shift to Renewable Energy Resources

Again, there are difficulties. The standard definition of resource and reserve is in terms of technically and economically recoverable. This is actually a limitation that the renewable energy resources hit very early on. They are technically feasible most of them, but are they technically and economically usable? The answer, by and large at the moment, is No.

Shift towards hydrogen as a fuel

This is not stupid. Technology exists by and large. Electrolysers now for producing hydrogen are very efficient. The type of electrolysers that were developed under the last EEC Energy Research and Development Programme are indeed very good, but that work has now been shelved on the basis that the research and development has been done, the prototypes exist and it is now up to industry to build them which it is not doing.

Stop cutting trees and replant more

New techniques for CO_2 disposal, getting it out of the way. My own feeling about CO_2 disposal, where there has been discussion about it, we are talking about sticking it into the deep oceans or burying it in old oil/gas wells, and one of the objections are that you cannot be sure that it is going to stay there and all the rest of it. I do not think that is the difficulty at all. I think a large part of the problem, if there is a problem, is to slow down the release of CO_2 into the atmosphere to something that the system can cope with and change the time constants. I think that is probably more important than encasing it for ninety five million years or whatever.

Global CO_2 emissions over the last thirty years show that the Pacific basin has cut its CO_2 emission quite strikingly. That is highly industrialised. Western Europe has sort of peaked, as has North America.

Global Warming: The Debate
Edited by Peter Thompson with the assistance of John P. O'Hara
© 1991 Strategy Europe Ltd. Published 1991 by John Wiley & Sons Ltd

The problem area, if we can speak of it like that, as has been said and as everybody knows, is the developing countries, Eastern Europe and USSR to different levels.

Consider a coal fired power station. It takes in about 10,000 tonnes a day, it produces 1,200 megawatts of electricity and it releases actually about 35,000 tonnes of CO_2 to the atmosphere. One molecule of CO_2 per atom of carbon. 35,000 tonnes a day of anything is a hell of a lot to cope with. Once we start talking about dealing with CO_2, collecting it, concentrating it and storing it, we are into big business. We are into very large scale technology. Do we want to capture all of it? I think the answer is going to almost certainly be 'no' because the engineering task of doing it is quite large.

We model plants for simulation purposes. A power station from the outside looks like a large lump of concrete and everybody knows that there is a furnace and there is a turbine generator. It is actually a very complicated piece of equipment and, once you start drawing out the feedback loops and start modelling this system, you look at it as a control problem and you wonder why the thing works at all sometimes. How is it stable? You have three feedback loops and recycle loops generating heat to feed the different stages of the turbine. Consider this conventional plant as 'case one'!

Consider now a proposal for the same plant, only this time with CO_2 collection. This is 'case two'. It is one of the trendy versions of this process where you feed in 10,000 tonnes a day of fuel again. You actually separate oxygen from the air and use the oxygen to drive the furnaces. Why do that? Because air is 80% nitrogen and why handle five times the flue gas volume that you have to? You are just enhancing your problem by a factor of five. If you take the nitrogen out of the air then, for one thing, you get no nitrous oxides and, for another, you make the problem more amenable.

However, this gives you problems in the boiler and what you can then do is recycle CO_2, in principle, back into the furnace to control furnace temperatures, but this is interesting in itself because it now changes the chemistry of what is going on in the furnace in a way that we do not actually know because the CO_2 will decompose into carbon monoxide and oxygen at the furnace temperatures. We now have a different combustion process. That has to be investigated, it cannot just be plugged in, it has to be checked to see that it will actually work.

The excess CO_2 is separated and, what we tend to take and most others tend to take as the reference case, is the cooling of the CO_2 and then compression to turn it into liquid CO_2 as the final product. It is a nice clean reference case because we understand compressors and we can do models on them. Therefore, we can get a very good picture of what is going on. Then the CO_2 goes to disposal – more of which later.

'Case three' is a similar process except, instead of just straight liquifaction and oxygen combustion, we used the other sort of standard proposed unit which is scrubbing the stack to remove the CO_2 using solvents (like MEA).

In very broad terms, if we take the standard case one as a power station 500 megawatts capacity, nominal efficiency comes out at about 35.6 which is a fairly run of the mill, bog standard industry power station. It will produce about 464 to 465 megawatts to the grid.

Case three, which was the MEA scrubber system, needs power for running the scrubber. You need power for the CO_2 liquefaction and you then end up with, because of the flue gas desulphurisation and so on as well, the actual power station efficiency reduced somewhat. You will end up with a net efficiency of about 26% which is not all that horrible. There are many, many power stations on the national grid that are running at 26% or less.

In Case two, which is the oxygen separation, uses a lot of power for producing the oxygen, but you have no power to the scrubber and you have extra power for the CO_2 liquefaction because the difference between Case two and Case three is that Case two is removing all of the CO_2 and the SO_2 that is in the fuel. Case three is only removing about 90%. You end up with an efficiency again of about 25% to 26%. Not all that horrible at all and when we started doing this sort of analysis, my instinctive reaction was that we were going to be down about 10%. That was my gut feeling that it was going to be stupid. But it is not.

If we go to more advanced cycles, with higher efficiencies, we can end up with power stations that are around about the best that are currently in use, with no CO_2 release as gas to the atmosphere. It is technically not all that daft, but I still worry about the volumes and the tonnages.

Once you have done all of that, we reach the point where we have now got this liquid CO_2 – what are we going to with it? That is a very good question. There are basically three proposals, though an additional one is actually gaining in interest and is what we call CO_2 chemistry where we use CO_2 as a feedstock in combination with methane, for example – which is a lousy feedstock anyway – and try to reform the CO_2 back into something more usable by combining it effectively with natural gas or whatever. There are certain indicators that this is not as stupid as it sounds. Again, it sounds stupid because if you burn methane, what do you get? You get CO_2 and water, both of which are highly stable. That is the reason why you get them. However, there are some indications that catalytic process may make it attractive as a possibility.

The other traditional uses are sticking it into the oceans, and it is either going to be perfectly safe because the oceans are relatively stable at depths greater than 2 kilometres and so you can stick it in. The CO_2 will then liquify on its own, it will sink because it is more dense than water and will slowly diffuse out at depth and it will recirculate slowly back up to the surface again in due course, or will convert into other things on the way up. The alternative view is that it is going cause havoc down there because it is going to do all sorts of nasty things and we are going to have these globules of liquid CO_2 which will kill all sorts of life that is there. I do not know. I would be willing to bet quite a large amount of money that nobody else knows either. However, it is one of these sort of areas where, again, research is needed before we would suggest doing it. It is not a cheap process, it depends where you put your pipelines. To use in Europe or even in the UK, or even in Ireland, which is as close to the edge of the continental shelf as you can get, you have to go quite a bit offshore before you get the 2 kilometres depth. Therefore, there is a transport problem as well.

The other is to use abandoned oil and gas wells. Again, you get people who say no problem: this is the sort of thing that we desperately want to do. We have all these holes in the ground that have been fully exploited or whatever, and we could pump this in and it would be perfectly safe. Then there are those who say that this may very well be true, but what happens if you have a leak and you can get this CO_2 effectively vaporising as it comes up with all of the consequences that would have. You would get an earthquake, or the sort of explosion you would get when landfill gas decides it is going to come to the surface suddenly and lifts your house up or your town.

Then, the final use, is the standard use which we use as a driver for enhanced recovery techniques. However, this presupposes that you are close to a functioning oil well which has reached the stage that it is going to need enhanced drivers.

That is a quick Cook's tour of the technology. I did feel, as I started this, that we have had a lot of talk and discussion of what we should do, but nobody had mentioned the possible ways of doing it. As far as the international co-operation is concerned, very largely this is being driven through IEA and we have already had quite an extensive talk about that.

There are also other discussions like the European coal and steel community has got concerns in this area and there are side discussions such as EC and Japan debates and probably USA/Japan debates, also USA and EC discussions and so on. Basically trying to pick up on each of these points as we come through and investigate the possibilities. What are the ways of separating the CO_2? There is liquefaction, there are membranes, there are the scrubbers. What are the techniques that we can actually address? We do not really know. This puts us back into the problems of what do we do? The answer is that there are lots of things we can do in ten years time, but we cannot do it now. It is the standard large scale energy problem. There are lots of things we can do in ten years time. Once we have five years research to make sure that we can actually do them, and that puts us back another five years, so we are talking about fifteen years really. I look forward to the rest of my professional career in this!

6

COAL: A POSITIVE RESPONSE
FROM AN INDISPENSABLE FUEL

Malcolm J. Edwards

Commercial Director, British Coal

Perhaps we ought to start at the root of the problem which underlies much of the argument. In just a hundred and fifty years to the year 2000, humans will increase six-fold to 6 billion. We, that is you and me, now far exceed any other of the large mammals. End to end, we would stretch to the Moon and back twelve times. It is surely a subject for astonishment and relief that this most profligate increase has not already caused some planet-wide catastrophe to such a complex balance of a world that has taken 3,000 million years to evolve.

For thirty years or so, the feeling has been growing that some disaster like this ought to happen, that we deserve it considering what we have been up to. Is it all about to happen? Global warming has been casting itself for that role. The battle lines have been presented apparently so clearly. On the one side, the two greatest qualities of life that distinguish the rich from the poor, the present from the past – easy access to convenient and fast transport, easy access to abundant and cheap electricity. Fossil fuels, carbon rich dominate both. Oil has a virtual monopoly of transport, coal and oil together provide over half the world's electricity. Both have grown as the world has grown richer.

Oil for transport accounts for more than three quarters of the increase in CO_2 emission during the 1980's here in the UK. Use of coal in power stations worldwide has increased by no less than 50% in the past fifteen years. Together, oil and coal provide 70% of the world's energy. Add natural to that, because natural gas burned at average efficiencies, plus the odd CO_2 rich gas field around the place, plus methane leakage, all add up to a formidable greenhouse contribution. You get the total fossil fuel contribution to world primary energy to nearly 90%.

There is no convincing scenario at all that the world could avoid using similarly vast quantities of these fossil fuels for the foreseeable future. Is all this about to run into the buffers? Could the results of continuing to burn fossil fuels in this way be more unacceptable than ceasing to burn them? Is the choice that stark?

We at British Coal sell 75% of our production to power stations. That is just a dull average. Power stations in all the developed countries burn 75% of the steam coal consumed there. For most of the past seventy years, the British coal industry has not had its economics easy and it has realised that, to survive, it had to put as much effort into increasing the value of the product as into reducing its production costs. We recognise that improving the efficiency of coal use is the greatest key to improving the economics of our coal. Self-interest argues that way.

Our experience would suggest that it should be possible to disentangle the essentials on either side of this global warming debate and try and fit them together. Now that is our objective and that is our positive response to what is a very difficult challenge. For businessmen and especially for anyone in the fuel business, there is no option now but to try and identify the consensus of global warming. Global warming may have become a political reality before it became a scientific hard fact, but for us it is an unavoidable fact of life. The public do not appear, at least at present, to be willing to wait around to see if things really do get uncomfortably warm so that they can have the scientific certainty

Global Warming: The Debate
Edited by Peter Thompson with the assistance of John P. O'Hara
© 1991 Strategy Europe Ltd. Published 1991 by John Wiley & Sons Ltd

that something should have been done twenty years before to prevent it from happening.

The scientific debate in these pages is certainly vigorous, but in the middle of it there are items on which there is agreement. It may be the earth's natural greenhouse effect which makes our planet habitable, but atmospheric concentrations of man-made gases are increasing significantly. Predictions of global warming have, to date, been based on models which are the product of much expert endeavour, but which are still imperfect, incomplete and unreliable. There is a need for further research on many parts of this exercise. This is not on some arcane fringe pursuits, but on central issues like the role of oceans and clouds.

It is still far from clear whether, in climate terms, we have as has been generally assumed so far a fragile world, or a robust planet capable of and indeed creating its own solutions to the many problems all we humans are imposing upon it. Certainly, things are a lot more complicated than they appeared when this debate was in its state of primitive innocence. We can measure most greenhouse emissions, but we do not know if they are significant. It is all so intensely frustrating to an age brought up to believe that everything observed has a demonstrable, quantifiable cause and result. If we can marshall such immense scientific resources for the United States space programme, for the Gulf war just recently, surely we can take by the scruff of the neck all the multitude of separate national research efforts into climate change, sort them into a coherent programme and drive them to establish the essential facts, in something closer to five years rather than fifty.

What is at stake here, as was said yesterday, are the very central economic springs of modern civilisation and progress. We all need to be far more sure before we radically change a direction of development which, in other respects, has been remarkably successful and beneficial. We just cannot do nothing while all the research goes on. What should we do while we are waiting? Well sensible things that are either economically beneficial in themselves or at least have only minimum penalty.

Certainly, pushing very hard on getting the Montreal Protocol to deliver everything we think it ought to do. Getting a far better grip over population growth and that is probably the most important of all. Linking an end to rain forest destruction to relief from debt payments. Both population growth and deforestation will be essential to deal with probably what is the most difficult of all the problems that we might find – that is soil erosion. The other half of the greenhouse, the CO_2 half and all its problems, remains. Common prudence argues that the scale needs to be reduced, but in a way which allows us to continue to enjoy the benefits of cheap transport and cheap power.

To be effective, the actions we initiate need to be precise, well targeted. At present, I think they show some alarming signs of being neither. It is a fact that faced with any high temperature but ill-defined problem, politicians feel compelled to react in some generalised way to demonstrate that they are doing something. That is why there has been so much activity on a subject very close to my heart, that is carbon tax. The examples where such a tax has been introduced so far give anything but encouragement about its effectiveness.

The original Pearce study, which started so much discussion in this country, was very balanced and comprehensive. It makes no sense if the whole of an environmental impact of a relevant activity (here we are talking about energy production and use) is not tackled to the whole. If it is not, then wrong economic choices are guaranteed and, because the investments are large and long lived, in the energy business those mistakes will still be around twenty years from now. It may be all very difficult, but we do need to decide amongst ourselves the relative environmental merits of the various fuels on a comprehensive basis. We have talked a great deal about the fossil fuels' contribution to CO_2 production within the phenomenon of the greenhouse, but the mechanisms and effects cannot yet be measured.

However, the next hydro or tidal barrage scheme may flood some very special landscape, a steep rise in European gas demand will certainly bring increased leakages of that very potent greenhouse gas until Russian engineering is sorted out. Oil spillages are a certainty, but their occurrence is quite unpredictable and waste from nuclear power stations is uniquely hazardous and remains so well beyond the time or life of any previous civilisation.

Renewables, to everybody's surprise, have great problems of their own. After all, five square miles of 18 metre windmills may generate as much as a fossil fuel station when the wind is blowing, but they are not the Seventeenth Century Dutch painting that most of us want to have in our back drawing room.

Carbon taxes, just to pursue this subject which is close to my heart, will not alter fuel choice in any serious way. All they do is to change the relative balance of income of the fuel slightly. Here you come to one central problem – fuel switching is not a policy to deal with the greenhouse phenomenon. Coal currently generates about 45% of the world's electricity in return for 7% or 8% of the total greenhouse gases. Those countries which need more electricity are likely to produce a great deal of it from fossil fuel, mainly coal. It is, in fact, the one macro fuel with a resource and cost base able to sustain the rise in power demand which is commonly forecast.

Oil has much the same carbon characteristics, even if we succeed in establishing the regime in the Gulf which can offer steady and predictable oil prices and, if Russia, which is the world's largest producer of energy, manages to put its own production on to a stable base.

Gas use, on anything like the present projection for power station investment, is bound to drive all gas consumers into Europe, into a heavy dependency on the largest and next closest source, which is Russia, and that means very great investment in the existing pipeline and in another which, on current estimates, requires a 50% increase in prices to remunerate. That will defeat any credible carbon tax differential. It has been so helpful over the past week, British Gas have concentrated our minds on this great dilemma just in the nick of time by putting up their prices by 35%.

Sizeable growth in nuclear I do not feel is essentially feasible and what we have now is being called into question even in France where it became a sort of substitute state religion. In this country, the power from the uncompleted PWR will be more than twice the cost of the fossil alternatives and not even the boldest of taxes people think can reverse such an enormous gap.

The real danger about all this sort of debate is that it obscures the straightforward actions that can be taken now to address the phenomenon in the energy sector, whilst we await the results of the research. The rich west is profligate, I think, in its energy use – not necessarily inefficient, but just profligate. I cannot help feeling that really effective selling, really active promotion of energy efficiency is going to have some impressive results rather than the sort of generalised modest energy tax that many have in mind to salve assorted political consciences.

In contrast, however, as we have said before, all the aspirations of the third world for recent homes and living standards and so on, are energy intensive. A quarter of the world's population have no electricity. You cannot conserve what you do not have. The private motor car, especially in cities, is the greatest greenhouse disaster of all with conversion efficiencies of about 15% and hydrocarbon carbon monoxide and NO_X emission to add their rich blessings to CO_2.

There is an interesting exercise that was done as part of the Californian vote which failed. The total contribution to CO_2 emissions from a battery driven car charged with electricity generated in a conventional coal station, is already a third less than a petrol driven car. With combined cycle coal, that CO_2 would be halved, NO_X emissions would be reduced by a factor of 20 and carbon monoxide and hydrocarbons by a factor of 100.

We all know that the costs of replacing oil in the transport sector is impossibly large, but it does seem to me that there are some promising new technologies which are still oil based, which would reduce emissions and increase efficiency. They do seem to me to be strangely neglected by the manufacturers. It is a great pity because cars have only a five year cycle and a basic technical change gets results quick.

What about coal and, in particular, coal fired power stations? The positive response from your friendly neighbourhood coal industry is all about increasing efficiency of generation and serious consideration of direct CO_2 abatement. If successful, both could have a very real effect here and around the world in reducing greenhouse emissions without reducing economic progress.

The first thing to describe is something which is not perhaps generally appreciated. We have become stuck in this country with the view of the conventional PF station as being irredeemably 37% efficiency, including FGD. There is a great deal of evidence now, in Europe in particular, that the efficiency of conventional PF stations can be raised into the forties and this is done by essentially high quality engineering and higher specification and some of the less conventional cycles. It is a basic simple technology which is known in and out and, therefore, any changes that are possible there can be applied without any hesitation at all.

Looking further than that, within five years, by novel techniques of coal combustion, coal gasification, or combinations of the two, coal fired combined cycle power stations will be available. They will be generating at efficiencies similar to those of the natural gas combined cycle plant now, but they will be able to draw on a much larger, a more flexible and lower cost resource base. We are talking about minimal SO_X and naturally low NO_X and at least 20% less CO_2. That plant will not involve some recondite technological skill unsafe in the hands of under-developed countries. That plant will be simple, small, robust, inherently safe and not fussy about the coal it has to burn. We are not only concerned to help develop this plant, we can and will provide all the necessary technical advice for this, just as we do for all other types of coal burning plant and, in my experience, that advice in many ways is more important than the hardware.

This leads me to the most important single opportunity for reducing greenhouse emissions in the energy sector quickly. The truth is that, so far, the developed nations have shown little practical ability to help the under-developed avoid repeating the same mistakes in energy use in their evolution towards prosperity. Much of the technology is already there. It is simple and robust, tried and tested and could revolutionise energy efficiency and reduce greenhouse and other emissions, but is only available from the west and for hard cash or loans at high interest.

If we are to deal effectively with the double problem of the inexorable rise in demand for energy in the third world and their current inefficient methods of using it, we have to decide unequivocally, about the resources we are prepared to apportion to transfer from our part of the developed to the under-developed world. It is a fact that, at the moment, only in the former East Germany are we seeing this problem being tackled in a thorough and comprehensive way. In five years, energy use there will be transformed from, quite simply, the most profligate in the world to among the most efficient. We need just this effort elsewhere, but on a much wider scale. We really do have to overcome our financial and institutional inhibitions in dealing with the less fortunate of the world because they hold in their hands the easiest, cheapest, quickest solution to so many of the greenhouse problems that worry us.

Just in case engineering developments do not prove to be enough, we are looking seriously, for the first time, at this radical solution of direct abatement. In very simple terms, all this great argument is about a very small imbalance, just 3 gigatonnes of carbon when the forests remove 50 from the atmosphere and the oceans 200 a year. What we have done, in fact, is to slightly disturb the natural cycle. We should look at restoring the balance. It is for that reason that last year we did propose, and we have now obtained, international support – There are fourteen countries involved – for very radical reappraisal of the economics of direct CO_2 removal. It is removal from where it is most concentrated which is power station chimneys.

Perhaps we are most enthusiastic about disposal in the oceans which already safely store something like 10,000 times the annual CO_2 imbalance. The research is very encouraging, but we could achieve some great results by simply stimulating the natural cycle that is already there, by enhancing the growth or ocean organisms which will take up more undissolved carbon, sink harmlessly to the ocean floor in the process, I hope, doing the whales a good turn. All this shows how wide the problem is and the opportunity. This greenhouse of ours does seem to be more full of undefined problems than most parts of the global property we all share.

Every self-respecting business can help. Certainly, it costs efforts, it costs management and money, but self-interest beckons. The more those in business help, the better the advice that will be available to the bemused politicians and the fewer mistakes business will have to suffer as a result.

7

NUCLEAR POWER: A PARTNER IN CONTROL

Mark A. W. Baker

Executive Director, Corporate Affairs and Personnel, Nuclear Electric Plc

I would like to begin by telling you a story about an imaginary country.

There was once a Kingdom where they dreamed the dream of a healthy growth of electricity generation, combined with a falling level of carbon dioxide emissions into the atmosphere. In the Kingdom of Urania the people set out to lead the world in reducing their emissions of carbon dioxide and making them fall quickly. They identified as their main contributor the electricity supply industry and set about growing the nuclear component of their industry very rapidly from 20% to 70% over seven years. Fanciful you may think, but they reached the target and carbon dioxide emissions from the electricity supply industry fell dramatically to a very small fraction of their level in year 0.

That would be a success story to tell the grandchildren about, a successful challenge to the problem of global warming but, of course, it is just myth isn't it. We have to deal with hard realities. Urania's valiant effort would not be enough in isolation. The greenhouse effect, and I should say here that I am not at the moment arguing whether it is real or not, is a worldwide problem for which only global solutions can be appropriate.

Let me try to put the issue in context. At global level, carbon dioxide constitutes more than 60% of the so-called greenhouse gases. Most of this is released by fossil fuel combustion in the energy sector, including transport. Carbon dioxide from electricity generation by fossil plant alone amounts to something like 12% greenhouse gases, nearly 20% carbon dioxide emissions worldwide.

What are renewable energy sources and the nuclear industry doing to help the situation today? Quite a lot really. Hydro and nuclear combined generate something like 37% of the world's electricity and save the emissions of over a billion tonnes of carbon a year. Nuclear on its own saves something like 450 million. However, this contribution is not enough and not growing fast enough to offset the problem as it is perceived. Let us just remember the scale of the problem as set out by the IPCC in the Working Group 1 policy makers' summary which commented that:

> "Atmospheric concentrations of the long lived gases: carbon dioxide, nitrous oxide and the CFCs adjust only slowly to changes in emissions. Continued emissions of those gases at present rates would commit us to increased concentrations for centuries ahead.

They went on:

> "We calculate with confidence that the long lived gases would require immediate reductions in emissions from human activities of over 60% to stabilise their concentrations at today's levels. Methane would require a 15% to 20% reduction."

To achieve stabilisation at today's atmospheric concentrations would need enormous efforts and it is hard to believe that it can be achieved in the medium term. If that is right, and if the greenhouse effect is real, we are already committed to abnormally fast rates of change of temperature affecting agriculture, wildlife and coast lines and, perhaps, having dramatic effects in terms of climatic extremes. All of which, to me, suggests that, as a matter of no more than common prudence, the world's

Global Warming: The Debate
Edited by Peter Thompson with the assistance of John P. O'Hara
© 1991 Strategy Europe Ltd. Published 1991 by John Wiley & Sons Ltd

nations should be starting to change their ways quickly over carbon dioxide emissions.

However, if the wealthy countries, either individually such as the UK, or in groups of countries such as the EC, do not start to take effective action what expectation can there be that there will be action, in the developing countries? Before we look at possible world futures, what are the main contributions to Britain's share of output of greenhouse gases today?

The electricity supply industry has been the biggest contributor since the mid 1970's. In fact, from the early 1980's onwards, we had rather a good record, but the trend seems to have changed now and has started to go up again. Why is that? I think one reason is that the rapid growth in the contribution to carbon dioxide free power generation from the nuclear industry in Britain has slowed down but the contribution that is currently made is very significant. More than 50 million tonnes of carbon dioxide emissions, or over 15 million tonnes of carbon, are saved by existing nuclear capacity – something like 10% of the UK's total emissions.

So much for the past and present, what of the future? On the global scale, it looks to me to be very difficult to face us with hard decisions. The IPCC's 'business as usual' scenario, involves continuing spread of higher levels of energy consumption through the world, combined with modest levels of economic growth and an almost inevitable population growth. On this basis, carbon dioxide would double between now and the year 2040. On scenario B, the energy shifts substantially towards gas and large efficiency increases are made. On scenarios C and D, major steps towards renewable energy sources and nuclear are made, either at the beginning of the Twenty First Century or at the beginning of the second half of the Twenty First Century. The words 'renewables' and 'nuclear' are in the IPCC report – they are not mine.

The IPCC looked at the consequences of the 'business as usual' and other lines in terms of sea levels and I do not need to remind this audience of their views on the effects in terms of land loss, regional climate change and other consequences. What is worth pointing out is that current trends are still pushing us along the 'business as usual' path. At the

Montreal World Energy Conference, global energy consumption was seen as growing by between 50% and 75% by the year 2020, mostly in developing countries with rapidly growing populations.

If the whole world were to move to the average current levels of consumption in the industrialised countries, by the end of the next century global energy demand would increase by a factor of 5. Fossil fuel resources would be absolutely inadequate to meet this demand I think and, even if they could, I do not think the environmental consequences would be readily acceptable.

What can and should be done? First, and obvious we need to look for substantial savings in energy demands through stringent conservation measures and major improvements in the efficiency use of energy. On what might be regarded as an extreme view, you could just about achieve a constant total energy use per capita if the industrial countries halved their average per capita consumption to around 3 kilowatts per head by the year 2100, and the developing countries did no more than double theirs to about 2 kilowatts. However, it seems to me, that shows just how much is asked of the industrial countries and the immense challenge facing the low income developing countries if they are to prosper while, at the same time, containing the potential for global warming.

Incidentally, you might also like to consider this. If each citizen of China were able to switch on the equivalent of just one extra domestic light bulb, a modest enough improvement in all conscience, world carbon emissions would be increased by the equivalent of 30 Drax B 2,000 megawatt power stations if coal were the fuel, something like the total installed capacity in this country.

World problems in the future are tough, but I think the implications at home are tough as well. The government has announced its policy of reducing carbon dioxide emissions to the 1990 level again by the year 2005. The implications of the Toronto Agreement which involved UK participation, but to which the UK were not formally a signatory, would be tougher: a further 20% cut in levels by the year 2005.

The Labour Party policy was stated in a useful document produced last year 'An Earthly Chance'.

The implied carbon dioxide target contained in that document, is 158 million tonnes of carbon in the year 2000. The same as the current government target, but five years sooner. It should be noted, however, that the Labour Party believe this target may involve a cut of only 10% or so on forecast emissions. If we look at forecasts, assuming business much as usual for the UK level of carbon emissions, we see a picture which is not so rosy. D R I McGraw Hill, Cambridge Economic Metrics and others, including the Department of Energy, have all forecast the level of carbon dioxide emissions in the year 2010 will be about 20% higher than those of 1990 on unchanged policies. The Department of Energy's low scenario gives a level in 2005 which is 12% higher than 1990.

If there is no positive strategy, private or public, and if there is no upward movement of relative energy prices so that there is no particular incentive placed upon individuals or industry to invest greatly in energy saving, we could easily imagine the volume of carbon dioxide emission per unit of national income continuing to decline only gently. In which case, I suggest, it is going to be very difficult to achieve the government's target for carbon dioxide in the year 2005. Even if all the new electricity were to be in the form of the most efficient carbon dioxide minimising combined cycle gas turbine plant imaginable. (There are substantially less carbon dioxide emissions per unit of power generated by gas than from coal but nuclear electricity produces only a minute fraction of the carbon produced per kilowatt hour, compared even with CCGT's and, yes, that does include carbon dioxide emission from uranium mining, fuel fabrication and reprocessing.)

Renewables – tidal wave and wind for example – are, of course, non-carbon producing forms of generation but are not yet fully developed. We do not see how they can make a major contribution in the short to medium term. Let us consider what might happen to UK carbon dioxide emissions under modest economic growth into the next century if outgoing generation plant was replaced wholly by gas-fired plant. This extreme example would spell the virtual disappearance of the UK coal industry, the electricity supply industry will not have done enough to secure the achievement of the

carbon dioxide target for the year 2005. Emissions would still be above the Toronto target.

However, if there were a major focus on conservation and energy efficiency on both the supply and demand sides of energy outside the electricity supply industry, then perhaps up to 10 million tonnes of carbon emissions could be shaved off the UK figure. Within the ESI, you might perhaps achieve a further 6 million tonnes of carbon emissions saved by investment in combined heat and power schemes and renewable energy sources. With the implementation of those measures, it may just be possible to reach the 2005 target without any new nuclear capacity.

But to maintain economic growth thereafter, as is necessary for greater national prosperity in the next century, inevitably requires a further energy demand which will find emissions pushing up again. We may be able to hit the target, but I do not think that we can hold to it.

If you looked at a hypothetical programme which replaced all outgoing capacity with nuclear alone, you would get a very different picture. Please note that I am not, repeat not, advocating an unbalanced programme of that sort, but it does illustrate the possibility that by restarting a nuclear programme after 1994, on even modest proportions, we may be able to maintain a healthy balance of use, of coal, gas and nuclear and, therefore, meet the necessary environmental targets at the same time as keeping a strategic balance between indigenous fuels. In a sense, nuclear power may enhance the scope for other energy sources to be included in the fuel mix.

For example, substituting the negligible carbon dioxide emissions from nuclear power for the more significant releases from gas fired generation could actually allow coal a better future. Nuclear power could thus assist in ensuring continued diversity of UK energy sources.

Before I conclude I should like to revisit my imaginary country, Urania. As you probably realise, it is not entirely imaginary. It actually happened. The country was France. The fall in carbon dioxide was in large measure a reflection of a systematic and rapid programme of nuclear power station construction. France took the proportion of nuclear power in its electrical power mix from 20% in 1980 to 70%

in 1987, and reduced its production of carbon dioxide from electricity generation from around 21 million tonnes of carbon to 4 million tonnes – a reduction of 80%.

In fact, the increase in nuclear power over that period now accounts for a total saving, on an annual basis, of something like 45 million tonnes of carbon a year compared to what had been emitted if oil fire generation had been chosen to produce the much higher levels of power demand that have arisen by the end of the period.

To sum up, I regard the challenge of the next century as being to ensure better living standards for our descendants and for those of our global neighbours while, at the same time, implementing policies which protect the world against some of the adverse consequences which science has suggested may follow.

We in the nuclear business do not claim to offer the sole means of achieving such a goal. Nevertheless, we do see ourselves as an essential element in maintaining a healthy balance between the use of different fuels and in meeting the environmental targets which may be essential to the ultimate survival of this plant. In short, I see nuclear power as being an indispensable partner in control.

8

THE VITAL ROLE OF ENERGY EFFICIENCY IN REDUCING CARBON DIOXIDE EMISSIONS

Stewart T. Boyle

Energy & Environment Programme Director,
Association for the Conservation of Energy

Eighteen years ago, the term 'energy efficiency' probably made people feel that you were asking them to take a walk on the wild side. It is fair to say now that energy efficiency is something which everyone is in favour of. The International Energy Agency, mainly on oil security reasons, is clearly in favour. The coal industry is in favour and the nuclear industry is in favour. Virtually every government is in favour. Everybody is in favour, but is it going to happen?

This morning I want to answer some key questions because, I think, without answering some of those key questions we will not be able to come to an overall answer about the purpose of this conference. I think the problem has been so far, to take account of particular industry sectoral interests as against the overall picture.

The first question, clearly, is the size of the carbon dioxide reductions. How much and how quickly?

You have seen the statements on the IPCC reports which indicated what it would require to stabilise concentrations. Clearly, those sort of immediate reductions of 60% are impossible. You cannot switch off fossil fuels. The has been an attempt, by a number of people, to set in some areas what are called 'ecological limits'. The idea of setting some limits beyond which it would get extremely risky to go and both Krause and also Kellinga and Schwart, who gave a paper at the Second World Climate Conference, developed this idea further. They agreed that it is important to keep within boundaries rates of climatic change, rates of sea level rise, and overall temperature increases. One study, by the

latter researchers suggests limits of 2° rise above pre-industrial levels and a rate of increase of less than 0.1°C per decade.

Setting an ecological limit for this sort of temperature has quite a major implication because of what it would mean globally. One suggestion split between the developing and the industrialised countries, is along the lines of the following: in setting an overall carbon budget of 300 gigatonnes over that period and taking a pragmatic view, and splitting that fifty-fifty with the developing countries and the industrialised. The sort of scale of reductions required which globally would be returning emissions to current levels in around fifteen years time, 20% reductions by the year 2015, and beyond 50% reductions by the year 2030.

Clearly, those figures would be higher for industrial countries and lower for the developing countries. The developing countries, for example, would be limiting their increases to around 50% to 100% of current levels, by the year 2030 or so, before returning emissions to current levels.

Similarly, scenarios produced by the EPA show that if we are to bring down emissions to control the levels, fairly substantial reductions are required. There is an implication of delay. That is one very important fact that came up in the IPCC process.

A delay of twenty years and then going ahead with a 2% per annum decrease in carbon emissions has a major impact in terms of the equilibrium temperature outcome. The concentrations in the atmosphere go above 460 parts per million carbon dioxide alone, whereas an immediate move towards a 2% per

Global Warming: The Debate
Edited by Peter Thompson with the assistance of John P. O'Hara
© 1991 Strategy Europe Ltd. Published 1991 by John Wiley & Sons Ltd

annum decrease keeps us below 400 ppm. I am pleased to hear that virtually everybody on the panel said whether we call it 'no regrets' or the 'precautionary principle', we should at least make some steps or do some things now, despite the scientific uncertainty.

The second question was what are the options available? What I want to do is, very briefly, refer to each of those and give some feel in the absence of energy efficiency, how much we could achieve in terms of carbon dioxide reductions.

Let me deal, first of all, with the switch to non-carbon fuels, essentially nuclear fission and renewables. There has been a great deal of analysis carried out over the last eighteen months. A famous or infamous, depending upon which side of the fence you sit, piece of work by Keepin and Kats took three different world energy scenarios and showed that in all of them, despite very substantial nuclear programmes, on its own nuclear would not achieve the kind of carbon reductions required.

Even with a medium growth scenario, we are still into a very large programme. The International Atomic Energy Agency itself carried out a number of pieces of analysis for the IPCC process. One of these showed that in what they regarded as optimistic, but non unrealistic (that is how it is described) increase of power stations in the OECD of 240 to 400 gigawatts over the next fifteen years, carbon emissions would still increase 60%.

Of course, the point that must be made here is that renewable energy is in the same boat. In the absence of efficiency, controlling demand, you cannot build enough wind, tidal barrages etc to achieve the reductions needed.

If we look towards fuel switching, let me remind you again the relative carbon emissions from different fossil fuels. The point, of course, has been made that although there may be gains in switching from gas to coal, you have a problem there about the extent and how much you can actually achieve even with a very aggressive programme. As we have seen with British Gas over recent price increases, every country increasing the use of gas, particularly the power sector, would obviously lead to some pressure on demand and a knock on effect on price. However, subject to a number of caveats, including the control of methane releases, it clearly could have a bridging role in a number of countries in a transition to a lower carbon future.

On the transport sector, also looking at alternative fuels, we are obviously not in the same position of being able to bring those on stream quickly. A substantial number of the options available actually do nothing for reducing carbon emissions. Methanol from natural gas does no more than play at the edges and, at best, it suggests a 6% decrease, but in some instances maybe an increase. With a number of the other options there is actually an increase. It is only if you move to hydrogen from non-fossil fuel, electricity, or electrical vehicles from the same sources, or utilisation of bio-mass resources, that you get substantial reductions in CO_2 emissions.

Moving to the advanced coal combustion side, improved efficiency on the combustion side is another option that has been talked about. Once again, you can go through that. It is important to put it in perspective. I would support the government funding British Coal's Topping cycle research, but with the best will in the world if that is successful and, even taking optimistic assumptions, we are talking about a 15% to 20% reduction in carbon dioxide emissions per unit of electricity, even if that comes through. That on its own will do no more than improve CO_2 emission levels at the margins.

Briefly on carbon sequestration, I am not an expert on forests. In looking at the literature it is very clear that to have more than a small percentage impact on overall carbon emission levels, you are talking about significant reductions in deforestation rates which, in itself, is not easy. Secondly, very substantial increases in the amounts of plantations would be needed. Greg Marland of Oak Ridge National Laboratory has talked about 700 million hectares to soak up most of the fossil fuel related carbon dioxide emissions. Frankly, nobody believes the viability of that. Just look at the implications of bringing those on stream, the management of them, the economic aspects related to that. I think a more pragmatic approach, as proposed by Tirpak of EPA, would suggest that a fairly aggressive but realistic programme could probably reduce carbon emissions in the order of 5% to 10% over the next half a century.

What role has efficiency? Let me say first of all, in response to the most important point made by Helga Steeg, that there is a big difference between the technical potential of energy efficiency and the current market potential. That is very clear, and I thought it would be useful just to explain why there is such a big difference.

There are first of all market failures. It is not a free energy market, it is not an energy market where there is perfect information, perfect competition, everybody has access to capital, and where there are no monopolies etc. We do not have that situation and, in many instances, there are clear market failures for efficiency options which, if one were to go down that route, would provide a better rate of return than building power stations or other supply options. The removal of those which, in some instances, is relatively easy and other instances more difficult, we can substantially increase the potential for efficiency.

We then have the whole area of the cost, the true cost of energy, the issue of pollution. In adding in that, then you can yet again substantially improve the economic use for energy efficiency and to some extent, renewables.

What role can, realistically, efficiency have? Part of the clue for this is in looking at what happened in the past. Helga Steeg indicated that there was a very significant impact in OECD and other countries. An analysis for the period 1979 to 1985 for the European twelve countries, indicates what happened in terms of energy intensity and energy demand, and the role of energy efficiency. Economic growth pushed it up but still, even in that last six years, a significant overall impact for improved energy efficiency occurred. Towards the end of that period, and since then, there has been a considerable slowing down, but I would say that is due to a combination of reasons. Government programmes have rolled back and clearly price is a major factor.

Looking to the future, I think we have to separate out the short term, (by that I mean fifteen to twenty years) and the longer term, because in many of the modelling analyses that I have looked at, you tend to get a very different picture and answer when you look at those two. In the first fifteen to twenty years the results are much more detailed, much more specific.

One example is an eight-nation study by Battelle Memorial Institute which showed under the base case assumptions, 'business as usual', a substantial increase in the order of 20% to 25% of carbon dioxide. It went on to show the reductions that you would achieve, mainly through fuel substitution and energy efficiency. The bulk of that, around two thirds, came from energy efficiency. The nations in the study were relatively representative of East European and OECD countries. That is very much the pattern for a lot of the analysis over a short term and that is certainly one of the themes that, in the short term, in the next few decades, efficiency is probably the option that you could do most on. You could start tomorrow. People could go out and buy compact fluorescent lights straight away, but you could not build an advanced Topping cycle or nuclear power station straight away. Therefore, there is a question of scale and timing on this.

In the longer term, the scenarios to 2050 to 2100 obviously are increasingly uncertain and we must take the results with a pinch of salt but when comparing the range of options available, the role of efficiency (transportation efficiency and other efficiency gains, particularly in buildings) is still very important.

This is all very well, but will it happen? What are the economic implications and will this occur other than in a very nice scenario? In twenty years time, will we be further forward? To answer that and leave you with a policy agenda, I think I would very briefly say that it is very important that you understand the differences, both in philosophy and the methodology of the different modelling approaches. There are two basic greenhouse gas modelling approaches. You have such big differences between, on the one hand, what some people call the $20 bill lying on the pavement – which is that energy efficiency is so good, you ought to do it anyway even if global warming is not happening – whereas, at the other end, some people are saying that it will bankrupt their nation. There does not seem to be any sense about why there is such a big gap between the two. The reason is that the methodologies are different, as well as the assumptions.

One way is to do what is called 'end use engineering modelling' – a sector by sector approach, measuring relative and net costs of various largely technological options. It is a prescriptive approach. It is saying 'we have a problem and here are some specific solutions to these problems'. It acknowledges market imperfections which are currently inhibiting the uptake of these.

For the United States, what you tend to find for that type of analysis is that compared to the current cost of the energy system, a substantial number of options are at negative cost. Doing the efficiency options, in comparison with carrying on with the status quo, by this form of analysis a lot of that comes out as negative cost. Only when you go beyond, it is a 15% to 20% reduction in US CO_2 emissions, that you move into actual net costs.

That is one approach. The other approach is, of course, the macro economic model and it is based much more on mathematical relationships, relationships of energy prices, GNP, income and the relative elasticities between those. Clearly it must be heavily based on data sets, particularly on the 1973 to 1985 data sets. It is a descriptive approach. It is really based on the assumption that individuals like you and I know what the situation is and will opt for the best solutions. It attempts to evaluate the actual willingness of you and I, as consumers, to purchase these new technologies by looking at what we did in the past and understanding those relationships.

Very clear difference in philosophy and one of the more well known scenarios last year came up with the figure, which many of you remember, of $3.6 trillion to reduce United States' carbon emissions by 20%. That would be the long term equilibrium cost by the year 2100.

I think it is resolving these differences, the major philosophical differences, major technological and data inputs here that is the key to me to moving forward in what has become a very arid and sterile debate with no attempt to try and communicate between the two. Obviously, one is tempted to say 'let us use the best of both' and, indeed, that is already happening. There are a number of tie-ups between both communities. I would say that is probably the most productive way forward, to use the best of both because there are pluses and minuses of each.

Let me conclude. The technical potential and, indeed, even the economic potential of energy efficiency, however one defines that, will not be achieved as things currently stand because there are a wide range of barriers to achieving this. I will just pick out several. Many of these you will be familiar with.

On the consumer side, a number of people are known as 'first cost sensitive' that is those who will not be able to afford the capital investment to make the improvements in efficiency which would be needed, even though the running cost would come down dramatically. Obviously, innovative financing schemes, opportunities for tenants to get the landlords to invest in efficiency would improve that dramatically.

On the energy producers' side, you will recognise the trait amongst the energy industries and partly it is no fault of theirs because that is the way they were set up. That is what they have been asked to do is produce energy. That is starting to change and, in the United States, we are finding that there is a whole move away from that approach where there is an attempt to provide energy services which may be with new power stations, but is increasingly with other options such as energy efficiency.

Price is a key factor. The true cost of energy must be a central part of any agenda in achieving the potential of energy efficiency. But I have caveats. On the role of carbon taxes, you need large carbon taxes on their own to get big changes in the consumer. For some consumers, particularly those for whom either the costs are irrelevant, or in fact they simply cannot afford to make the investment anyway, however high you increase the price, it is not going to impact on them. Therefore, high energy tax is a blunt instrument on its own, but I think it is important for energy to pay its true price.

The role of utilities is important as is the role of government in giving clearer signals about our revised expectations of them. An evaluation of even the limited improvements in some of the utilities in the United States showed the estimated outcome of demand side management programmes under least cost planning. It estimated the summer peak demand, even as things currently stand, to require around eighty power stations less as a result of those programmes. That gives some indication of the likely benefits of that approach.

Let me finish with a policy agenda, several of which I have referred to:

Paying the true cost of energy, which means the role of externalities, energy taxes and removal of subsidies for fossil fuels and nuclear power.

Setting high minimum standards of efficiency which increase over time.

Giving clear guidelines to the energy companies on integrated resource planning.

Allowing innovation to thrive. That is obviously very much a judgement here. Breaking up monopolies and access to consumers for provision of energy services. The role of innovative financing, third party financing and marketing programmes has been shown to be pretty critical in getting a high uptake of some of these efficiency technologies.

Getting the energy research and development contribution and balance right, which is clearly is not at the moment. Less than 15% of total OECD research and development budgets are given to conservation and renewables. The bulk is for nuclear power and fossil fuels.

Information and training programmes.

Finally, and crucially, government commitment and leadership. That is what is missing, to some extent, in the debate in some countries and, in particular, in the United States. It is not so much the technology. It is not so much the skills and abilities. It is not so much that supply industries have not got the ability to change but, without that leadership, clearly they will fight their corner. Therefore, we will have the atomic industry saying 'let us have a bit of everything, but make sure we have nuclear power as well please'.

The International Energy Agency is obviously much more reflective of the suppliers in the countries as part of its make up and, of course, its historical role is based on oil security. The coal industry says everybody else is to blame but me, and really we want to help the whales so let us have more research. The oil industry is often curiously quiet in some of these discussions.

Do we embark upon five more years research, or do we take action now? My firm belief is that we need to take action now, although the results of the scientific analysis of the IPCC clearly left uncertainties, the risk is sufficiently great to act. We have to accept that precautionary principle. I think being sensible and having an objective outlook and discussion on the economic side of things, we would conclude that it is possible to overcome some of these market barriers and achieve at least a high proportion of the significant efficiency improvements.

The reality is that the energy industries will not change if there is no obligation on them to do so because clearly they make their money by keeping us addicted to the fossil fuel drug. I do not blame them for that because that is their business, but we are, in my view, in the 1990's at the start of the transition away from fossil fuels. That is something which will take many decades to even move slowly towards. One thing for certain, energy efficiency will be the crucial option in that transformation.

QUESTIONS

(1) QUESTION: Nick Eyres
                 Energy Technology Support Unit

I just very briefly want to describe some work that has been done by some of my colleagues recently for the European Commission and this is of the sort of energy economic model that Stewart Boyle described for the UK and looking at the costs of carbon dioxide abatement. What came out very clearly was that the economic potential for CO_2 abatement is very large, certainly well in excess of 30% in the UK. Most of that, of course, is energy efficiency, but there are also cost effective applications for co-generation, for some fuel switching and for some of the low cost renewables, notably bio-fuels and wind power.

It would seem to me that the heart of the global

warming debate should, in the short term, if we are thinking about a "no regrets' policy be what policies need to be adopted so that those cost effective resources can be used in the short term.

(2) QUESTION: Mr M Cooper-Reade
                  Eastern Electricity

May I firstly say how refreshing I found Helga Steeg's presentation in bringing some realism into the energy debate. Unfortunately, so often in these debates the only role seems, for electricity for instance, in reducing greenhouse gases is in cleaning up generation or improving the efficiency of electrical appliances. Of course, we should do both of these and, in fact, the introduction of CCGT in this country over the next five years will significantly improve generation emissions, but the most significant contribution that electricity can make is, in fact, in replacing inefficient fossil fuels at the point of use. Because of the much higher efficiency of the electrical technology, there are many applications in which electricity can reduce greenhouse gases and we believe that, in this country, by the year 2005 we could actually reduce greenhouse gases by 10% by fuels switching to electricity.

I am interested to know whether the IEA, in their deliberations, allow for any fuel switching to electricity at the point of use?

ANSWER: Helga Steeg

Yes, of course. The question what is the source base for electricity generation? In itself, electricity is a clean fuel, but what the question is from what source is it to be produced? Generally speaking, yes fuel switching is being considered and, yes, generally speaking we have made in the IEA, without much noise a major shift that more gas to go to the electricity centre, but there are still of course some countries who have more coal in the electricity generation. The picture is not black and white here.

ANSWER: Stewart Boyle

In some industries clearly this can be useful. However I challenge you to convince me that you as an industry can compete with a house heated by a gas condensing boiler. Then we could have a dialogue. Fuel switching to electricity is relevant in some industries but we must keep a sense of perspective.

(3) QUESTION: Pier Vellinga,
                  Ministry of Environment,
                  Housing and Physical
                  Planning,
                  The Netherlands

I have a question for Helga Steeg and Stewart Boyle on the projections of energy demand increase of 20% over the next ten years and I would like to start with the point made by Professor McMullan that the energy demand has more or less stabilised over the last ten years in OECD countries, in North American as well as in European countries. How come the energy outlook of IEA projects a 20% increase of energy? I would like to have comments from both Helga Steeg and Stewart Boyle on this. Do we foresee a more energy intensive economy? It may be so, but I would like to have some answers.

ANSWER: Helga Steeg

First of all, I do not think it is correct to say that there has been no energy growth in OECD countries, let alone the developing world and the Eastern European countries. The amount of GDP being used for energy growth has, of course, been considerably reduced. But it is not true that there has been no energy growth in the past.

Of course, also there have been ups and downs and that depends very much on the economic situation. In the beginning of the 1980's there was a recession. In a recession, everything grows less than when you an economic recovery and it is clearly seen in the United States where there has been, in the oil sector in particular, some decrease in demand. Why has it been? It has very much driven by the recessionary effects.

If, what everybody hopes that we are already at the valley of decline of the economy and if the economy steps up again then there will be an increase. As you know, if the United States is going to get on the road to economic growth again, this will have a major impact on Europe and also on Japan, and the developing world on their economic growth.

To cut a long story short, yes there has certainly been some considerable decoupling between economic growth and energy demand, but this has very much been influenced by economic growth as such. In the electricity sector one has to say that electricity has, in all our countries, grown much stronger than total primary energy let alone oil and gas. On average, electricity growth, in all our countries, has been about economic growth.

ANSWER: Stewart Boyle

The question goes to the heart, I think, of the methodology and the use of data. I was trying to bring that briefly in the difference between the two modelling approaches because I do not dispute that in some countries there has been, over the last few years, a reversal of trends in the period through the late 1970's and mid 1980's and there has been an increase.

The question is whether you think that is going to extrapolate, that you can continue that through for another fifteen years. What type of economic growth and what industries are growing? That is the problem is you use a macro economic approach, you do not necessarily know what is going on in the sectors, especially in the industrial sectors, that may be driving that. You may get the economic growth, but it may be in the services sectors which uses very little energy.

I know that the IEA are no longer just taking as accepted what the member countries are giving in terms of their energy projections any more. I think that is a good thing because I think what tended to happen is the IEA members gave what were always very high projections from the industry side and you simply had to add them up. You are now doing better analysis. However, in the UK for example, their submission to the IPCC included such absurdities as quadrupling in the chemical industries over the next two decades, a doubling in the steel industry. For those from overseas, we're shutting down a steel factory in Scotland. These are absurdities and they do not relate at all to what is actually going on on the ground.

In the UK, there has been a relatively stable energy demand and, in fact, a fall in carbon dioxide emissions over the last twenty years. I would be very circumspect indeed in extrapolating over the next two decades. My feeling is, for the UK, that we are likely at most to see somewhere between, under the 'business as usual', a 0% increase and 10% at the most. That is my feeling and I think there are a number of people, even in the Department of Energy, who would share that view.

COMMENT: Professor McMullan

Just a comment on what my data actually was, in case there is any remaining confusion. It was a plot of energy against GDP, energy per unit of GDP, so it really was energy intensity. What it showed was this decoupling, a very strong decoupling in the Pacific basin, particularly in Japan. It is interesting in the Japanese case in that Japan showed no sensitivity to the second oil shock at all. Their energy intensity just follows the trend line straight through, but it did show a hiccup on the first oil shock, and the measures they took then carried them through the next one.

The rest of the world reacted quite violently to the second oil shock as well. In the UK case, we have got quite extensive decoupling and it depends which way you do the sums, there is either 38% or 44% decoupling between energy and GDP, but it has been at the expense of manufacturing industry.

QUESTION: Professor Michaels

As the climate models have become more sophisticated, after the writing of the IPCC document, the net projected warming has tended to drop considerably to 1.9°C. With your ability to generate estimates of the costs of remediation and the costs of inactions, there must be a temperature at which it becomes not necessarily a good idea to do anything. Can you give me an estimate as what that temperature is?

ANSWER : Stewart Boyle

That is an impossible question because to answer that you would have to know a whole range of things, in which at the moment there are big uncertainties. For example a key thing which I ought to have referred to in the presentation in an economic analysis, is the cost of doing nothing. Clearly, that in a sense is your base line to compare doing these policy actions. If you sit back and wait for it to happen, wait another ten, twenty years or beyond, what would the impacts be?

At the moment, we have only got very crude numbers for that, some of which were produced by IPCC, but the data for that is growing. There was a number quoted I think something of the order of $500 billion to raise a number of sea walls around the United States. I think you are going to need an awful lot more work in that particular area to give you the answer that you are looking for. I think I have taken the approach which is, I am not a climate modeller and if you wanted a more specific answer then Pier Villenga would probably give it to you, but from my perspective what I have tried to suggest is that quite a number of these things are worth doing anyway.

Given that we have got such a large potential for economic energy efficiency now, it would put us in a much better place if we take those first steps.

The difficulty is that nobody is actually doing it. We are not moving forward on those 'no regrets' or 'precautionary principle' policy options.

Part III

The Transport Debate

9

ISSUES FOR ACTION

Michael C. Roberts

Director of Energy Studies, PA Consulting Group
Vice President, Institute of Energy

In many ways, today's situation was forecast by Rudyard Kipling about seventy years ago on completion of the first air ship crossing of the Atlantic, when he said that:

> "We stared at the opening verse of the opening page of a chapter of endless possibilities."

However, despite that, there are some people who continue to believe that global warming does not matter despite what is going on in the transport debate. There are people who continue to believe that, as far as transport is concerned, there will always be plenty of fuel. We are here to debate whether global warming matters or not in some ways, but one point about the availability of fuel I would like to make is that comment is possibly correct. But if you look back over the last forty years or so, there have been many occasions on which there have been very serious interruptions to the supply of fuel and transport fuel in particular.

Despite all that, the key need is to improve the efficiency of usage and thereby reduce the total dependence on fuel and thereby reduce the contribution of pollutants to the atmosphere which comes from the transport sector. The pattern of usage with regard to the direct and indirect usage of fuel by transport is that two thirds is what I call direct, that is just gasoline and diesel in the engine, fuel oil in ships, or kerosene in aeroplanes. One third is what I call the indirect usage which goes towards maintenance, the raw materials which go into the manufacture of the vehicle, the infrastructure roads, railways and the losses in generating energy particularly electricity which, in turn, is used to drive

vehicles and used to drive the machines that make it. These figures are based on the UK.

Direct usage represents 28% of the total UK's energy consumption. When you bring in the indirect usage, we are talking about 42% of all the energy used in this country. It is also 70% of our oil and that pattern is similar to other parts of the developed world. The cost represents £16 billion to UK Limited every year, out of the £39 billion that we spend on energy. It is one and a half times domestic usage. It is two and a half times UK industrial usage. You might like to reflect on that and think of all the exhortation industry has received over the last fifteen years about using energy efficiently, and just ask has transport received the same degree of exhortation?

If you accept that manufacture of raw materials of the vehicles is about 11%; if you accept that a vehicle has an average life of about ten or eleven years then, doing the arithmetic immediately shows that the energy involvement in manufacturing vehicles is approaching twice what it uses, what the vehicle uses, during the course of its operating life. Again, that is a pointer to some of the areas in which we should look for attention.

Road traffic accounts for 85% of all this; air traffic 11%, and rail 4%. It is growing: freight transport is up 66% in the last ten years. Due to faster speeds, the usage per tonne is up 35% and the number of miles is up 22%. On passenger vehicles, it is not quite the same: the energy used per thousand passenger kilometres is down a bit thanks to improvements in aerodynamics and improvements in energy performance, but the mileage is up, so the total is up.

Global Warming: The Debate
Edited by Peter Thompson with the assistance of John P. O'Hara
© 1991 Strategy Europe Ltd. Published 1991 by John Wiley & Sons Ltd

That growth represents about 4% per annum. At the same time, average journey lengths are increasing together with a continuing drift from rail to road and from public transport to private transport. With regard to the pollutants that contribute to greenhouse warming, the areas where the motor vehicles contributes are certainly carbon dioxide, nitrous oxide and nitrous dioxide. Road vehicles do add carbon monoxide which is toxic and contributes to global warming. You also get a small percentage of unburned hydrocarbons coming out of the combustion engine which adds to that.

Looking at some of these individually, you can see that transport is putting, in terms of direct transport, 120 million tonnes of CO_2 a year in the UK's atmosphere. Electricity generation is only about 200 tonnes. If you transfer the bit of that which is the generation of electricity used for indirect transport usage, you have the two getting very close to each other.

Turning next to oxides of nitrogen, from 1977 to 1988 the totals are reasonably stable. Looking at the change from the individual source, transport sticks out – with 20% increase – but decreases in most others. Also, the transport figure is just about 50% of the total. If we look at carbon monoxide, you get a more startling picture. Transport is the only one to increase over ten years 4½ million tonnes a year, out of a UK total of 5½ million tonnes.

Those figures convinced me that it is a major sector.

I would like to draw your attention to a few facts. Firstly, government support for this sector. We have the Department of Energy who tend to regard transport energy efficiency as the responsibility of the Department of Transport. When you talk to the Department of Transport, they regard themselves as a regulatory body and, as a result, we have a vacuum which requires attention.

Of the total, land transport accounts for 85%. Cars are 80% of this and, at the same time, engine size tends to be increasing; car size is increasing; the numbers of cars are increasing; and the energy improvements which have been made by manufacturers through design and other factors are being cancelled by those increases. If you look at the pollutant pattern, unless we take more action, the pollutants: carbon dioxide, NO_x carbon monoxide

and unburned hydrocarbon, are all going to increase significantly over the next twenty five years.

There is also substantial scope to work on the internal combustion engine. It has a potential efficiency of about 40% of the fuel put in it. Currently, it has achieved no more than 12%. First of all, you are losing a huge chunk through the cooling system and the exhaust system – nearly two thirds of it, so certainly there is need for development in those areas. Then we have the actual engine power with losses through friction in the engine, air and so on. You can then get 19% to the wheels with losses through the transmission system, accessories, axles and, finally, if you look at that, you end up with the 12% of useful work. That is the state of development at the moment.

I would just like to refer to a batting order of transport energy effectiveness. It had sea travel as one. It had canal traffic, inland water, as three. It had rail haulage as ten, and road vehicle as fifteen. Again, you can see, if we can go from road to rail to canals, it makes sense. When it came onto the three passenger categories, buses and trains and things like that are a factor of forty, private cars eighty and air transport two hundred and ten. That tends to concentrate the mind on a few things also.

These are the issues, which need probing fairly carefully, to achieve improvements for the future:

(1) Catalysts, knock out carbon monoxide, knock out the oxides of nitrogen (several types, they are easily poisonous) They do add to fuel requirements. They are not suitable for diesels and a fair amount of development is needed.

(2) Turning to the engine transmission, we hear talk of lean burn technology which actually reduces pollution. Currently, it uses a little more gasoline. Variable transmission so that one is constantly optimising the power of the engine with the requirements of the road wheels is reckoned to have a potential saving of 20% and, of course, electronic energy management systems can do quite a lot more and they are in their infancy.

(3) On operational issues, route planning, time of travelling, traffic management are fairly obvious

ones. There are two areas which I think need developing:

(a) The use of traffic controls to control the flow of traffic onto roads like, for example the M25 so that it does not get overcrowded and come to a crashing halt. If the traffic onto it was controlled, one would be able to get as much traffic onto that road now as would be the case if it had a fourth lane built all the way round it. It is a much cheaper way of going about it.

(b) There are similar things one can do in the airline field, with the use of computers, to stop these enormous stacks around Heathrow at peak times, and I am sure we have all been in this situation.

(4) Alternative fuels: diesel is about 30% more efficient than gasoline, yet only 2% of cars use them. Biomass to alcohol is part of a natural cycle. Carbon dioxide is produced, it is absorbed, and alcohol is about 15% more efficient than petrol in an engine. Then there are things like, getting further on, the use of hydrogen and (providing it is not produced by electric means), and then there is a need for battery development and one or two other things like that.

(5) Vehicle design: I have some examples of how aerodynamics can reduce the losses on lorries.

(6) There is a need for education and training in the way people operate their vehicles. Potential savings that could be achieved. They are not cumulative, you cannot add them together, but smooth driving compared with tearing about the place can save about 20%. Keeping to the seventy mile an hour speed limits throughout the UK would probably save 20%, but I am not sure it is that much. Certainly once you get above fifty or sixty miles an hour the consumption tends to go up by something approaching the square of the speed you are doing.

(7) Downgrading to smaller cars. A small downgrade, less than 200cc's is effective.

(8) Regarding maintenance – how many of us here have our cars regularly serviced?

(9) On a slightly different tack, legislation and government support is required in this sector. Sensible legislation and sensible support. We need technical standards. We need influences on issues such as to increase vehicle occupancy, as they have successfully done in the United States. We should avoid blanket taxation which, in my view, merely results in inflation. We should promote the use of technology to traffic management, as I discussed earlier. We should use fiscal measures to promote the efficient and the less polluting options and, above all, we should set dates for achievement of milestones, unlike the environment paper – the White Paper – which sets a target fifteen years hence without any reference as to how we are going to get there, how we are going to measure it, or what the interim targets are.

In conclusion, in my view not enough is being done in this area. The vehicle growth is tending to more than absorb the improvements to date. The rate of improvement may increase, but I do not think it will be enough without more action on this front and we should aim to achieve all this without resorting to either restricting legislation or penalising taxation.

Finally, let us not forget that the internal combustion engine is so far no more than 12% efficient. In imperial terms, and my apologies for those who have been brought up in metric units, this means that for every gallon we buy we use a pint efficiently.

10

THE RESPONSE OF THE MOTOR INDUSTRY TO ENVIRONMENTAL PRESSURE

Sigvard Hoggren

Vice President of Environmental Affairs, AB Volvo

I am not at all in agreement with the previous speaker on the 12%, especially as he said that the engine has an efficiency of 12%. It might be true of the vehicle, if you go from the engine to the wheels, but the engine as such has roughly 30% when you talk about an auto engine. If you talk about a diesel engine, it is about 43% to 45%.

I do not think I can really talk for the whole motor industry, that would be presumptuous perhaps, but you can look at this as a kind of a case report from Volvo and what we have done in recent years to meet the requirements from environment. We launched what we call the 'environment charter' about two years ago in an action programme and that contained a number of very important items.

First of all, we reported to our chairman in August 1989 the full final report of a job that had taken about eight or nine months with all Presidents of the big divisions, such as cars, trucks, buses, aerospace, a few others and myself. We stated that there should be an environmental policy for the group. We have had that ever since the beginning of the 1970s, but it was outdated and not quite meeting the requirements of today. We, therefore, had to change it and that is the first thing we did. I will come back to that and to the components of the environment policy because I think that is very important for what follows after.

Also, we presented something we call the 'guidelines for minimum Volvo standards' and that should actually be seen, together with a three to five year Volvo programme. These two together actually state that each president of every company in the organisation worldwide is required to see to it that

they have a three, five, perhaps six year programme for environmental actions in that particular company, for the products and also for production. They present that to their board and we, at head office, also get a copy. We, therefore, have a good number of copies on long range environmental action plans by now.

Every year, we have guidelines for minimum standards in the company. Within the long range programme, everyone is also required to report to his board and to ask, within the programme, what are you going to actually achieve during the forthcoming year – for example 1991. When I left the office last week, we had about half the organisation's reports on that specific subject.

Following that is a training programme. We started this very early in 1989 by calling a meeting for four hundred and fifty of our top and middle managers in our Swedish organisation and they were exposed to a two day seminar on some basic ecological facts, for example what is global warming? What is it all about? What are greenhouse gases, and what is the relative contribution? Also, what is actually happening to air, to water, how we do in our kind of actions, what we do in production and using the products, how do we contribute to things? They were given materials so that they could go on with this training programme in their own companies.

About two years later, we know that about ten to eleven thousand people had gone through basically the same training, not only managers but specialists and even workers along the lines. I think this absolutely basic if you want to be successful, and go deep

Global Warming: The Debate
Edited by Peter Thompson with the assistance of John P. O'Hara

into the problems because I think it is crucial that people who are asked to participate in the various actions should know the basis for it. Why do we do this? Why is it so important that we do things to the products and to our production programme?

In our head office, we have only three people and this is because if you want things done, see to it that they are done out there where the problems are. Each producing or sales company now have what we call the 'environmental councils' consisting of the top management of the company, if not all, at least the majority of them including the president of the company and some specialists. They meet on the single subject of environment and environmental concern. In these groups, they very often discuss these standards just mentioned.

To summarise the whole thing, we have what we call the 'environmental audit' and this is something which we have tried now for almost two years. This is a very efficient tool if you want to check out what happens, especially the production units. We have a few of them in the UK, one in Workington (when we bought the Leyland Bus organisation two years ago, so it is now part of our organisation. We have actually carried out an environmental audit at Workington) and Irvine in Scotland where we produce trucks. We are coming to them for an environmental audit later on.

In the particular case of Workington, I think they actually perceived what is essential about the environmental audit. It is not merely a control instrument from top management. It is an instrument by which you help the local plant manager, for example, to find how well he complies or does not comply with regulations, rules and conditions, and what should be done. It is up to him, and to nobody else, to see to it that we meet the future demands.

Let us go back to environmental policies. First of all, we try to develop market products with superior environmental properties which meet the highest possible efficiency requirements. These are not very quantitative terms, they are just ambitions or directions if you wish. Also, to opt for manufacturing processes that have least possible impact on the environment. That is production and manufacturing. We also say that we want to actively participate

in and conduct our own research and development in the environmental field.

In addition, which is rather interesting, we want to select environmentally compatible and recyclable material in connection with the development and manufacture of our products, and when we purchase components from our suppliers. This is rather interesting because sometimes it is easy for the company to do what it wants to its products but, in our case, we buy a lot of components from others and they have to meet practically the same environmental standards.

We have to talk to suppliers of, for example, paint. We are all in for water based paints so as not to release solvents, so please see to it that we co-operate in designing the procedures necessary for that. Also, try to apply a total view regarding the adverse impact of our products on the environment. This is a beautiful word, but what do we mean by 'total view'?

You could simplify and say 'do not solve one environmental problem by creating another'. An example for a diesel engine is that you want to get rid of the particulates. If you do that and nothing else, there is a risk for the NO_x to go up and vice versa. Of course, what you should do is to decrease both, or get rid of them altogether. Another example, if you want purify you want to use filters which are very efficient, but they require a lot of electric energy, so you create perhaps an environmental problem somewhere else. Also, people ask 'what do you think about the things you have outside Sweden?' We strive to obtain a uniform worldwide environmental standard for processes and products. This cannot be done overnight. We know that.

To take the example of a truck plant in Brazil, for example, we have said to them 'do your best'. At least you should start by trying to be the best in that particular business in Brazil and then, after that, we can perhaps talk about meeting other objectives as well.

If we take all these things together, you can very well argue that they are beautiful and good words, but if you stop here and say this is what our intentions are, they are rather meaningless I think. They should have a basis to stand on so that you can shape your long term programmes, your minimum standards and everything on the belief that this is actually what we think in the company and it is absolutely necessary that we follow this.

To go back to environmental auditing and the way you compose groups for this. I sit next to the corporate auditor who actually works for me, and he travels around with groups of people, specialists usually composed for a particular audit so that if you go to the car company, there are no car company people present for that audit, they come from trucks and elsewhere in the organisation.

Let me take a few remarks about the product. Our plant in Gothenburg is our largest plant with about twelve thousand people. If you include all the offices around it, it is the largest working place in Scandinavia. If you look at it, it is a site of emissions, so to speak, in itself. Our main problem is the emissions of solvent. Ground ozone and things have to do with the emissions of solvents. You have to try to get rid of that.

Just a few examples on how we can work on it: water based colours. In our plant paint shop, now working in a trial period, we have invested between £150 and £200 million. It takes away practically everything. We combine materials like water based paint. If you go inside the paint box, you do not see any human beings and that is because if you have human beings inside it you have to have very clean air, and if you have clean air you have to have a very effective ventilating system. In the old paint shop, about three and a half million cubic metres of fresh air was pumped into the plant every hour, and the same amount had to go out. That creates a problem because there is a very low concentration of solvents and, consequently, it is very difficult to care for. What you would like to do actually is to have a higher concentration, but if you have a higher concentration you can no longer have human beings inside.

So we have a fully automatic painting procedure now and theoretically at least, you can concentrate it ten times which brings down the amount of air to one tenth of what is was before. You can burn it and you can take care of it in many ways. In addition, we use for the end of pipe technology for the remaining solvent things like rotating carbon filters, silicone beds and various other things.

So it brings down the amount of solvent from the old days when the emissions from painting a car body in metallic paint usually meant an emission of about 10 kilos of solvent to the air. It has been brought down in the new paint shop to 1.2 kilos per car body. The car body, of course, is a very large thing. The total area of a car body is very close to 100 square metres, so there is a lot to paint.

There is something which we presented about one year ago in Geneva. We named it the 'Volvo environmental concept car' because we have put into one rather regular car all these things that we have today or will have in the very near future that meet some very specific environmental demands. For example, the three-way catalytic convertor which is now in all cars we make, more or less, for the Swedish market at least with an electrically heated auxiliary catalyst because that is the problem with a catalytic convertor. Usually when you start the engine, especially on a cold winter day, you find that it takes a certain number of seconds before the catalytic convertor is really efficienct and that can be helped if you have pre-heating.

Also, the flexible fuel engine which is something we have developed. We are not the only ones, but it means that you can have any kind of combination of, for example, petrol and methanol that you would like: 85% methanol, 15% petrol, or any other mixture. Environment friendly refrigerants, in the air conditioning units in a car, is usually where you find the CFCs in the car cooling medium. We are gradually replacing the CFCs by innocuous material.

In addition, CFCs are being replaced by more environment friendly alternatives in the manufacture of plastic parts. For example, the seats and many other parts which are usually the things we get from somebody else, but we see to it that they use other substances than CFCs for that particular ambition. Also, solvent-free underseal compound which is, if you use the old method, one place or one material in which you find a very high percentage of solvent. We now use another method which is called the 'put on hot' method, so to speak. You spray it on while it is hot. It cools down and that is it. No solvents at all.

To go to another branch, not necessarily cars, we have introduced in the truck plant in Gothenburg an entirely different way of painting the frames and axles. We use powder paint with no solvents present. The powder paint is attached to the axles by electrostatic methods and is very efficient. We use asbestos-free brake pads and so forth, which we have had for some time.

Finally, we have the chromic acid-free parts, mercury free relays. There is a drop of mercury sometimes to make, for example, the lamp in the lid work. A drop of mercury which we tried to get rid of because it moves slowly. Plastic parts marked for future disposal. We have realised, if you go to the production of cars, I can agree with our Environmental Minister in Sweden. I do not agree with her very often, but on this specific point she says – by the year 2000 she thinks, and we think, that problems from site emissions in Sweden will be over, more or less. We will be fairly down to zero at that time.

It is not only a matter of producing the car and using the car, it is a matter of how much raw material do you take out? How much energy do you actually use for the production of the car?

The previous speaker said that the average age of a car is about ten or twelve years. I do not know about other cars, but the Volvo is twenty one and a half years. After twenty one years, still fifty percent of the cars are on the streets, which is good or which is bad, because if you talk about the fast technical development it could be looked upon as a bad thing if you want to introduce new things. For example, it is not efficient to install catalytic convertors in old cars. We would prefer cars to be new.

We often get the question – how do you look at alternative fuels and the future? Today we have petrol. Tomorrow or in five or ten years, perhaps methanol or ethanol which is very interesting. We have, using outside experts, taken a look at 'from cradle to grave' thinking, from the moment when you extract raw material to make some kind of fuel, until is has driven a vehicle about, say, 100 miles. If you do that, and look at things like ethanol, for example, it is rather easy to calculate to get one amount, or one unit, of energy from ethanol, It take three or four years to produce it. It is not very good really.

Methanol is perhaps better. It could also be mixed with other things. We do not particularly believe in natural gas because of the rather low energy content and, consequently, you have to have tanks with very high pressure. If you go on, from let us say, five or ten years, I am now talking not necessarily about technical things because all these things are already there. You have hydrogen cars today. There are cars like that. There are also, of course, electric cars, but I am talking about a period of time when it is more or less commercially available and, perhaps, in ten to twenty five years you may have electric cars that can be used by all of us. Since there are so many problems connected with hydrogen, I think it will take thirty to fifty years until it is fully useful.

To summarise, we are producers of vehicles and, as such, we think your environmental responsibility lies not only within the use of cars. It is wider than that, comprising also of production and the final scrapping or recycling. I think we are only at the beginning. New engines, new fuels will have to be developed and this is basic if we want to continue using the individual vehicle for transport. Transportation, I think you will agree, is very basic. It is a very basic human need. It is even written among the freedoms in the Common Market. It is also so deeply rooted in human nature that it simply cannot be relinquished, neither in our generation or in that of our children or grandchildren.

11

THE NEED FOR SOCIETY TO MOVE TOWARDS ENVIRONMENTALLY SOUND TRANSPORT

Andrew Davis

Commercial Director, Environmental Transport Association

The modern car is, without question, a master piece. Its styling and comfort, its reliability and robustness are a testament to modern technology and engineering. We are justly proud of our achievement and we regard the motor car as a thoroughly good thing and, with all good things, the more we have the better. Why stop there? As cars are such a thoroughly good thing, we can do even better by using our cars as much as possible. Doubtless, we will achieve excellent results.

As we travel more, we construct more car parks and our cities get bigger. We, therefore, have to travel further and more often. This, in turn, requires more roads. Yet, despite grid systems, parallel freeways a mile or two apart, each with eight or ten lanes, modern cities in America are grinding to a halt. Cars are no longer our servants, they have become our masters.

The car which was started as a superb solution to our transport demands is, by its very success, rapidly becoming the major transport problem. We are all aware of the advantages that cars provide us. Car manufacturers constantly remind us. We can no longer ignore the mounting disadvantage of mass car usage.

I shall highlight several areas of concern:-

(1) Cars consume energy
Transportation is about 21% of world nonrenewable energy usage. It is also growing faster than both the industrial and the industrial commercial sectors.

(2) Cars produce noxious gases
In Britain, about 50% of the nitrogen oxide emissions are produced by road transport.

(3) Cars produce sulphur oxides
Another component of acid rain. These emissions will fall in Britain as more cars are fitted with catalytic convertors. However, as 8% of car journeys are under five miles and most catalytic convertors currently take several miles to warm up, their effect may not be as good as originally thought.

(4) Cars produce greenhouse gases
In Britain, road transport produces 24% of the greenhouse gas carbon dioxide. Motor vehicles are the major growing source of greenhouse gas.

(5) Cars are unsafe
Despite the efforts of motor manufacturers, Volvo in particular, cars are very dangerous. Cars kill people. Last year alone, forty thousand people were killed in America by cars. Although the number of injuries to car occupants is decreasing in Britain, the number of injuries to people hit by cars is increasing.

(6) Cars are unhealthy
Cars are the major causes of both low-level ozone and carbon monoxide. These gases accumulate beyond the World Health Organisation's danger levels in many cities of the world.

(7) Diesel driven cars produce tiny carbon particles
These particles damage both people and buildings. Motor manufacturers are having some success in reducing the diesel soot, but the increase in the

Global Warming: The Debate
Edited by Peter Thompson with the assistance of John P. O'Hara

number of diesel-powered vehicles outweighs all their efforts.

(8) Driving cars increases stress

Driving cars increases stress in humans without the related exercise. A very unhealthy combination. Driving reduces the amount of exercise taken in the ordinary course of daily life and, instead, exercise becomes a separate event. A work out at the gym, or a jog in the park. It is somewhat bizarre to see someone drive to a sports club to use an exercise bike.

(9) Cars are central to industrial production

Motor vehicle production still dominates the use of resources in industrial countries. The making and use of cars and trucks currently consumes about 60% of the world' oil, 20% of the world' steel production, 35% of zinc, about 50% of lead and 60% of natural rubber.

(10) Cars increase inner urban decay

As more people use their cars, their link with the community decreases. The use of the public domain is reduced to travelling inside a metal box along a road. They tend to care less about the areas they pass. The centre of towns are given over to surface parking. In towns, like San Jose, California – over two thirds of the land area is used for parking and access for cars. In such a landscape, walking is difficult if not unpleasant.

(11) The car increases social breakdown

Cars are beginning to have a serious psychological effect on people. Cars have all but taken over the road space, either for parking or traffic. Traditionally, in this country, children used roads as play areas and could explore their home town without fear. Surveys in England have shown that parents have restricted their children to their home streets and many parents drive their children to school. Nearly all parents cite the threat of traffic as the reason for doing so. Limited children become limited adults.

These areas of concern have been taken from the fifty or so industrial countries, but the image of the jam packed motorway gives us a totally false impression of the day to day experience of the average person in the world.

Nearly two thirds of the world's people meets their daily transport needs by walking. 20% use some form of public transport. About 14% use a bicycle. Leaving only 6% using a car. So 6% of commuters, if I can use such a term, use the car and 75% walk or cycle. Those 6% use 80% of the energy and that 75% use next to nothing.

I have briefly outlined some of the problems caused by our growing dependence on the car. The problems would not, perhaps, concern us if there were only a few cars. The damage could be contained within society and within the environment. However, because there are now about five hundred thousand cars, and their number is growing rapidly, the accumulated damage has become unsustainable. This is the fundamental problem.

(1) How did we get here?

We got here because of two central and inter-linked beliefs of western thought:

> The first is the belief that more of a good thing is, by definition, better. This leads to a rapacious use of the limited resources of the world.

> The second belief if that more individual choice brings more freedom. This fails to recognise the context in which people make decisions. At any given time, we can only make choices from a given set of options. We cannot choose an option that does not exist.

For example, if I want to travel from Ealing to Hammersmith, I can go by train or car. I have an individual choice. Let us assume I go by train. If I want to travel from Ealing to Harrow, I must go by car as there is no railway between these two towns. I have no choice. If I buy car for the Ealing to Harrow journey, I may as well use it for the Ealing to Hammersmith journey because the marginal cost to me is low. If enough individuals are beset with a similar set of circumstances, the Ealing to Hammersmith railway will be closed, thus reducing the service to others and producing a vicious circle. This is a classic case of an individual choice producing less freedom.

An environmentally sound transport policy rejects these two western beliefs that more is always better, and individual choice always results in more freedom. It replaces them with two other beliefs:

The first is that all societies must be able to sustain themselves and that they, therefore, manage demand if that demand becomes excessive.

The second is that greater freedom for the individual can often be derived from making decisions at a higher level.

For the industrial peoples of the world, it will mean an end of transport policy based on the internal combustion engine and the private car, and the beginning of a society based on walking, cycling, buses and trains.

(2) How do we do this?

First we can manage the number of consumers. The foundation of any policy leaning to sustainability is the rapid stabilisation of the human population and its later reduction. Any other action is futile without it.

Second, we can reduce the amount of non-renewable energy each person consumes. We need to strike a balance here between market mechanisms, such as price, and legal measures, such as controls.

The simplest way to reduce demand is to increase the price of non-renewable energy, by taxing it. Such a tax will have far reaching effects, cars would become far more fuel efficient very quickly, public transport will become relatively cheaper. It will encourage all of us to rethink our use of energy and other resources.

We can enforce the speed limits. We could install more stringent controls on emissions, banning new private vehicles that fall below a stipulated minimum miles per litre on the urban cycles, we can check car exhaust pollution as those cars go down the road rather like speed checks. We can control private vehicle access to high density areas. Here we can use a variety of measures:

– Road pricing

– Pedestrianisation

– Bus and cycle only roads

We can insist that day time parking for cars is charged at commercial rates with access open to all cars, thus ending subsidised company car parks and reducing all day inner-city parking.

We can improve the quality and availability of public transport, especially in Britain. In Britain, we can start by ensuring that all our bigger cities have rail links to the neighbouring cities. It is absurd that you cannot travel directly by train from Coventry to Leicester, or from certain towns to Milton Keynes. We can replace our terminus stations like Paddington and Liverpool Street, Waterloo and London Bridge by linking them together and, thus, improve the service remarkably. This has been done in many other European states. We need to follow the example of the Netherlands, Germany, Switzerland, by integrating our buses and trains.

We must improve facilities for walking and cycling to make our towns fit for living in again. In towns, cars should only be allowed on sufferance and not by right, especially in our high streets and residential roads. We do not accept pedestrians on motorways, so why do we accept through traffic in our town centres?

Cycling is the most energy efficient way of travelling and it should be considered the usual way of travelling in towns. Following the example of the Netherlands and Denmark where, in some cities, half of all non-walk journeys are made by bicycle.

Finally, we must focus our minds on where we locate our houses, factories, offices, leisure centres and shops. Without development control, new facilities will be built on green field sites. Thus producing low density sprawls like Phoenix, Arizona with seven people per hectare. This low density means that travel is limited almost exclusively to the car. This dramatically increases distance travelled between locations. It also makes it increasingly likely that people will have to use a car. People under seventeen will either rely on their chauffeur parents, or lose access to these facilities completely.

A town designed for sustainable living will need to have an equal number of work places as adult inhabitants. Thus avoiding the split between office cities, like London which are dead at night, and dormant towns, like Radlet which are dead during the day. This balance will reduce commuting. The town would need to be limited in size to ensure that all able bodied persons could walk to the centre or conversely to the countryside. The size limit would also guarantee an accessible green belt for all people. With the railway station in the very centre of each town, surrounded by the towns cultural, political, spiritual, commercial and educational facilities, we will be able to live again in safety and in harmony with the environment.

Although the day of the internal combustion engine is by no means over and the number of private cars worldwide is set to rise over the coming decades, the tide is already turning. Whatever the motor manufacturers do by increasing the miles per gallon, or by changing the pollutant the cars produces, we cannot sustain a world society based on the car.

Policy decisions made at the level of choosing, say, between unleaded petrol and electric cars are fundamentally flawed. They are like choosing your wallpaper for your bedroom while your house is on fire.

We have a choice. We can carry on as we are and face either ecological catastrophe or continuous fighting over the world's resources, or we can choose to live sustainably within the environment. Our path for survival is clear. We must have an environmentally sound transport policy and we must begin to develop it today.

QUESTIONS

QUESTION: Professor McMullan
University of Ulster

One of your proposals is tax. I happen to be very sensitive to petrol tax as a topic. I live in a rural community. The petrol tax seems to those who live in rural communities to always be part of these proposals that come from people who live in cities. In cities, what is the average mileage in the UK – something like 7,000 miles a year. The average mileage in Northern Ireland, where I live, and in Northern Scotland is something like 13,000 miles a year because of the remoteness and the requirement to use a car.

These are areas which are already in economic difficulties and any additional tax on fuel is going to handicap them even further. Yet, if you live in the city which is where these proposals come from, if you are only doing 7,000 miles a year or less, who cares what petrol costs? It is not going to make a difference, but it is going to penalise attempts to rejuvenate the highlands.

ANSWER: Sigvard Hoggren

If you want to know more about taxes, come to my country. We have quite recently added an extra VAT on gasoline so the price now is the equivalent of about 70 pence per litre. I think it is the highest in Europe, next to Italy perhaps. However, it has not really had any large effect on travelling habits so far. In the beginning, the first week, you can see some effects, but then it is back again to the same amount of driving.

ANSWER: Andrew Davis

There have been studies which have shown that the amount of tax would have to be so enormous to stop the addiction people have to being in their metal boxes that it would become disruptive to the economy. It cannot be the only thing and, I must say one thing, it is not a fuel tax, it is not a petrol tax, it is a non-renewable energy tax. It is not just for petrol, it is just a blanket tax on all non-renewable energy. We have to strike a balance between the fact that the bulk of the population live, nearly 85% of the population, in cities in this country and we have to strike a balance between where the energy is consumed and in reality, because very few people live in the countryside, to strike a balance between the usage and the options that other people have.

Economically speaking, if people want to live in outer Sutherland, which is a delightful place to live, or in some parts of Ulster, they have to make those choices themselves given the economic environment they are in. We must address the major problem which, to have a sustainable lifestyle, we have got to rid ourselves of using non-sustainable resources.

QUESTION: Professor McMullan

There are two points there. One is that there is a sort of a general myth that there is no tax in all of this. We pay quite heavy tax on fuel.

ANSWER: Andrew Davis

There is also a myth that people, on balance, pay for roads. On balance, in this country, roads are very heavily subsidised and so I would not go into that route otherwise you will find yourself on very sticky water. There have been countless studies recently which have demonstrated, beyond any debate whatsoever, that road transport is subsidised to the hilt in this country.

Of course, there are taxes on new cars. There are taxes on the fuel itself. We do not want to have specific taxes on the car. We want to have taxes that are linked to energy. Volvo is a very conscientious company, given the remit which it has, and they have been looking at these issues a lot longer than when it became flavour of the month. They have been driving down these avenues before. Not all companies in the motor industry are following these lines. They need to be encouraged.

As soon as petrol price went up in the 1970s, the size of car declined. As soon as the prices went down, the size of cars went up again. We need to keep the pressure on continuously to force all industry to be conscious of the price we are paying. It is not the economic price. It is the price of the damage we are causing to the environment in which we live.

(6) QUESTION: Mr J. Ruscoe, ENEA (Italy)

What I am interested in, in this particular debate and also in the debates that have gone on this morning, is the discussion between aspects of individual freedom and regulation, control, imposition of some form of authority. This is particularly appropriate in this debate in that we all agree that we should limit the access of cars to city centres. It has been tried in Hong Kong.

In Hong Kong there was a system of road pricing with cars and computers working out how many journeys they made. The system worked well, as far as I am aware, but it was stopped after six months on the grounds of civil rights because people did not like to be told where they had been travelling. This is a philosophical point, but one which the environmental debate raises in all its different aspects. It is something I would like, perhaps, to be commented on.

ANSWER: Andrew Davis

It is a very delicate debate. Whenever these social changes are required, we have to think very deeply about the ramifications. The Hong Kong implementation was a mistake anyway. They should not have done it the way they did, so it was a bit of a botch.

However, the central point is that whenever we come to catastrophe, we need to do it at a higher level than the single person, be it a village in previous societies or today. When we had epidemics in London, we dealt with the sewerage, only once the evidence became totally obvious, but we dealt on a social level. We restrained peoples' ability to just throw their rubbish out their front door. Before that it was quite normal to throw your rubbish outside and to flush your toilet, if it had one, out to your next door neighbour's land. They were quite acceptable things and it was your right to do so.

We have just got to understand where the balance between the individual and society in the world lie. I would suggest that, for people to drive internal combustion engines into the middle of this city, is putting the balance far too much on the side of the car. We must move, especially in this country, we must understand that the right of the individual loses us rights as a society when we take it too far. I think the balance in transportation, over the next ten years, will move to such an extent that people will understand that in their bones – they will not have to think about it, they will know that we must do the constraint.

ANSWER: Sigvard Hoggren

There have been some cities that have been rather successful in closing central parts such as Montpelier in France and a few others. Oslo is getting rather far also.

This is a very interesting discussion because, sometimes when you take part in a debate on alternative ways of transport, people say 'the main mission of the car is to take somebody from 'A' to 'B' or from the city to the city. I think there are so many other qualities. You can close things around yourself, you are sitting there, I do not have to mention all these other qualities.

When you say that 'let us go back by something else like the underground' you lose a lot of these qualities. We have suggestions in our city such as 'let us stop cars now entering into the central part of the city' and then they have suggested various types of trains to move around. The thing is that this would require a huge investment and who should pay for that? It would be decades before you can reach it and people are very hesitant to do that. As long as they are hesitant, they will keep using their cars.

The matter of financing the thing and also, one should bear in mind, the qualities. Sometimes you simplify the discussion by saying 'let us go by train instead of the car'. What are we actually talking about.

I am all for your suggestions on trains and I think we shall all advocate for large cities to be rid of cars, but we shall have to provide alternatives for people to go on, otherwise it will never function.

Part IV

Framework Policy and Legislation

THE RESPONSE TO GLOBAL WARMING, THE POLICY PROGRESS, IPCC AND PREPARATIONS FOR CLIMATE CONVENTION

Dr Pier Vellinga

Ministry of Housing, Physical Planning and Environment, The Netherlands

The fight against global warming and the debate about it is like the New York marathon: run annually by amateurs. With the outcome of the IPCC report, the starting shot has been fired, but this is not a race of 40 kilometres but over forty years at least. However, the rules of the game have not been established. As we all know, the initial phase of a marathon is the most difficult, especially when you are not sure whether you really want to run it.

I am happy to talk here about the international framework for the negotiations. I have been in it for quite a few years now, but the main reason I am here and was attracted to the programme is the active involvement and participation of industry and other sectors of society. Although we have started in negotiations, I am sure we still have to broaden and deepen the involvement of all sectors and, without that, we may even succeed as governments to get convention because everybody wants it for political reasons, but for it to be effective we need more days like this and we will need much more active participation from other people and other companies.

I will first talk about the United Nations framework, then about the state the negotiations and the controversial issues and thirdly, I will have a proposal for progress based on a two phased approach.

IPCC

We started yesterday with a presentation by John Houghton on the science working group 1. Not everybody is aware that there was also a working group on the impacts of environmental change, chaired by the Russians. This group indicated the potentially devastating impacts of global climate change.

The third group was on Response Strategies. This group has a steering committee on emission scenarios and legislative aspects. It had 4 subgroups: one on energy and industry, one on forestry and agriculutre, another group on coastal zone management and one on resource use management indicating what kind of adaptation possibilities there are and trying to explore the costs.

The IPCC report went to the Second World Climate Conference in Geneva 1990. There were some seven hundred delegates from one hundred and thirty countries, many of them with their Ministers, and they reflected on the IPCC report. The main conclusions were to accept the report as basis for international policy development.

The precautionary approach, or at least a concept of precautionary measures, was adopted. Although there are some uncertainties, the Conference concluded we should do the things we can right now.

They welcomed the stabilisation of CO_2 emissions at 1990 levels by 2000 by the industrialised countries. Not all industrialised countries have set their targets, all but one I believe.

Global Warming: The Debate
Edited by Peter Thompson with the assistance of John P. O'Hara
© 1991 Strategy Europe Ltd. Published 1991 by John Wiley & Sons Ltd

It was also concluded that developing countries need to take appropriate actions, but within economically feasible limits.

The Ministers decided to start negotiations for a global climate change convention. What would be the goal? The ultimate goal, as said by the Ministers there, is to stabilise greenhouse gas concentrations.

That is not easy but, we must look at it in the long term perspective. Everybody agrees that an ultimate goal for sustainable development would be to come to a certain equilibrium concentration on the atmosphere. It may be higher than before. The Ministers further agreed that the first step should be to stabilise emissions of greenhouse gases not controlled by the Montreal Protocol.

The final conclusion of the Ministers in Geneva was 'let us start negotiations' and actually the first round of negotiations started last month in Washington. It was not a very enlightening experience I must tell you. In IPCC there had grown a lot of consensus over the two years. Now carrying on these negotiations to the highest level is necessary. The issue is important enough. In Washington, however, a lot of new players entered the game. Professional diplomats from New York United Nations who had not participated in the IPCC process so far made the first negotiation round recover many issues debated before in IPCC. However, after two weeks there was sufficient basis to start working in two separate working groups.

Another phenomenon I witnessed in Washington was that the stakes are so high and indeed they are, that for just negotiation reasons a lot of countries did one step backward to get a better position. For example, there was initally some US opposition to mention the word 'CO$_2$' in the texts. On the other side, we also saw developing countries that said 'we first want money on the table before we start negotiations'.

I guess these are just natural reservations when you start to negotiate such a far reaching issue. It is not very encouraging at this stage, but I think in the long run we will overcome these difficulties. We still have six negotiation rounds to go and when you have six rounds to go, in the UN context this means you go slowly in the beginning.

This Inter-governmental Negotiation Committee established two working groups. The first is on commitments. On its agenda is limitation and reduction of CO$_2$ and other greenhouse gases and the enhancement of sinks and reservoirs. This working group is also addressing the situation of developing countries' vulnerability to climate change and the need of additional financial resources. This is a loaded agenda for just one working group. We may have to split in two later on but there are some problems with that, as developing countries cannot send ten delegates to negotiate in a number of separate working groups.

Another working group has been established for formulating the legal and institutional aspects of the convention including compliance, assessment and review, scientific co-operation, monitoring and information, financial mechanisms and mechanisms for the transfer of technology. Once the first working group has drawn up more substantive commitements, the second working group can include them in the convention. For example, the additional finances, would these be managed by the Global Environment Faciltiy of the World Bank or would they be dealt with in another way?

What are the controversial issues in the negotiation process and which issues will be with us for the next year and a half to come and, perhaps, for the next decade to come? Right now the initial difficulties are:

(1) agreement among industrialised nations on the stabilisation of CO$_2$ emissions by the year 2000, at 1990 levels. As you may be aware, all OECD countries, including the EC as a whole, favour this stabilisation at 1990 levels by the year 2000. These countries agree that this can be done reasonably well. It does not have a significant impact on the economy. However, the US has a different opinion.

(2) There is some controversy about either a comprehensive approach or gas by gas commitments. The United States is advocating the comprehensive approach, I think for very good reasons. If we really want to address climate change you cannot just focus on one gas, although it is 50%, 60% or 70% of the problem, but we must also take methane, N$_2$O and low lying ozone into account, and we should ao, for the most cost effective approach.

In the end, I expect there is not a controversy whether you make gas by gas commitments or comprehensive commitments. The European communities and the EFTA countries say 'we can do both'. Using a comprehensive umbrella, gas by gas commitments can be identified. This does help industry and other institutions to focus their minds. The outcome of the controversy could probably be a misture, not so much either comprehensive or gas by gas commitments, but a comprehensive and gas by gas commitment within a certain range. There is some flexibility in the international negotiations in this area.

(3) The third controversial issue is the additional financial resources for developing country commitments. In its extremes this controversy can be described by whether to say 'this amount of money is available for developing countries, please set your own priorities' (which some of them would like because they are 'short of money anyway'), or 'we industrialised countries take a positive approach, but we would like to see commitments on your side as well towards additional finances, maybe not in targets of CO_2, but in targets of energy efficiency increase, side by side with financial aid'. First there must be an assessment of needs, and channels must be developed.

In the negotiations, it is not easy to have diplomats discussing additional money, when it is spent mainly through industrialised channels. We need more private sector participants to discuss additional financial resources.

We are discussing climate change policy in th UN framework. This process will be slow and probably painful because there are so many other UN issues. The social and economic gap may dominate to make global agreement hard to reach.

What is happening on the regional context? The EEC has set a common target to stabilise CO_2 emissions by the year 2000. If you add up all the individual commitments of, say, Denmark, Germany, the Netherlands, UK, France and Italy, you can do it but there should also be some commitments from the Spain, Portugal, Greece and Ireland in at least reducing the growth of emissions.

The EEC has joined with EFTA countries in setting targets to stabilise CO_2 at 1990 levels by the year 2000. Maybe we should take more time in an OECD context to find solutions for the controversies between the US, on the one hand, and the other OECD countries, on the other hand. This has some drawbacks. We all understand that the developing countries want the industrialised countires to make some commitments, but it could be confusing to negotiate it separately. A lot of technical work can be done at OECD level, but final agreement is needed at UN level, to involve developing countries.

The South East Asian group has not been manifesting itself very strongly yet, but in an ASSEAN context a common approach is under discussion. In Latin America the RIO Group is recognised with Brazil being very active there. Some countries in teh RIO Group recognise that climate change may not be just another north / south issue. We are living in a changing world and also the blocks may change, thus the group of 77 of developing countries may not be the most effective tool to negotiate with the OECD countries. Brazil is taking quite a progressive point of view now towards OECD countries. This indicates a willingness to go on with policies to increase energy efficiency and reduce deforestation and advocate a substantive convention to be signed in RIO.

Then you have the AOSIS which is the Association of Small Island States, which is a very interesting group of countries who say 'we are so vulnerable' and they really press on OECD countries to take action to save their nations. The climate network of NGO's is very active. Then we recognise the industrial coalitions – we have seen Don Pearlman here who is the most outspoken person of this group. I would like to see some more coalitions take the same tone as Shell has been taking in these issues. I understand this major oil company takes the view that global warming is one of many major issues which have presented themselves to us, such as acid rain and limits to growth. We will have other issues in the future. Let us accept that we are living in a changing world. Let us take a pro-active approach as multinational.

My personal proposal is (but I have seen it proposed by others as well), that we should go for a two-phase approach. Phase 1 would be characterised by flexible commitments with a pledge and review process. Some nations are very cautious of real emission reductions in the future. If we look at the stabilisation issue, this can be done, but not all governments are ready to do it. It we can present suh targets in a flexible way with a pledge and review process, it may help governments to make a political commitment to curb the growth of emissions. Stabilisation of emission by industrialised nations is technically and economically feasible.

In this Phase 1, we are in bad need of sectoral initiatives from the transport sector, from the energy sector and the forestry sector. We should look at this first Phase as a learning phase for co-operation and negotiations because we still have a long way to go. We need many more new interest groups involved.

The second Phase would be detailed commitments and procedures. With a global cost effective approach, with fully professional bodies for monitoring and compliance. The establishment of international effective bodies is not done within a year and a half. That takes probalbly a decade. For monitoring and compliance and clearing house functions, an organisation such as the World Bank could organise the most cost effective approach. I could invite offers from countries or regions and finance the reductions.

I would like to end with a pledge that we need more international, industrial and sectoral initiatives and commitment. They are crucial for an effective policy. We need the automobile manufacturers to get together and set their own targets. We need the energy sector, we need the chemical industry and research and development institutions. Right now, in the Netherlands we are making progress on that.

Under the threat of energy taxes, under the threat of regulations, which is now under debate in our government and the public, under this threat industry has decided to come up with its own initiatives. For example the chemical industry has now made an agreement with the Netherlands government to increase energy efficiency by 20% over the next ten years. What this means in absolute CO_2 terms has not been committed, but given the likely growth this wll be very close to a stabilisation of CO_2 emissions in that sector.

The same with the glass industry. They are signing an agreement this month with the Netherlands government. Within the next ten months we will have over twelve sectors signing similar agreements (covenants) with the Minister of Economy and Industry and the Ministry of Environment.

In an international context, the Netherlands government is very much in favour of a regulatory tax. This would be a budgetary neutral tax. It would tax energy, but it would reduce income tax which is also giving an incentive to employment and other issues. This idea now supported by many hard line economists as well. Germany and France are interested in this regulatory tax. I know that the UK, with its privatisation of electricity, is not so interested at this stage but, in the long run, economic instruments are attractive, I am sure, to all industrialised countries, more so than regulations. At least, we will probably need these economic instruments to support the voluntary commitments taken by industry and, when you do it in an international way, industry will join us.

In the end, I think really to solve the problems of the 1990s, and to solve the confusione we are having now, we need a trialogue of governments, scientists and the private sector, laying the basis for the decisions we need to take to ensure a susatainable development.

13

A FRAMEWORK FOR SURVIVAL: MOVING BEYOND THE CURRENT APPROACH

Dr Michael R. Redclift

Reader in Rural Sociology, University College, London

The first part of what I have to say, I think I should emphasise, represents a personal view, although I think it is consistent with the ESRC's new initiative programme in global environmental change.

I want to start by looking at some of the things that we know at the moment about this debate. It seems to me that among the thing we know are, first of all, that global temperatures are governed by the atmospheric greenhouse effect. Secondly, that greenhouse gas emissions are rising. Thirdly, that these concentrations are linked to human activities. We also know some other things.

We know that the contribution of developing countries in the south to anthropogenic change is measured on a per capita basis much less than that of the developed countries. We know, for example, that the USA emission levels of CO2 are about five times the global average. We know that the developed countries contribute about three quarters of carbon dioxide emissions and the less developed countries about 25%.

We can see that there is a huge global inequality in the contributory factors.

We also know that, with population increase in the south in critical countries like India and China, that the level of emissions is likely to increase and this represents a problem in itself. But I think the debate about global environmental change and about global warming in particular, is rather different from the debate about sustainable development because sustainable development for most of the rich countries was about what happened or should happen in the south.

The difference is that global environmental change inevitably impacts on us. We are bearing the cost, or we might bear the cost, and we cannot evade the consequences. Most of the sustainable development debate, in practice, started with the assumption that, and even the Brundtland Commission to some extent was guilty of this, that there were marginal changes only required in the north, that the problem lay in the areas where environmental problems are most severe, particularly in the south where people are poorer.

I will add another thing which we know. If preventative measures are taken to halt or reverse global warming, there will be other tangible benefits. There are knock on effects, benefits, reduction in acid rain, air pollution, cleaner water, end use energy efficiency in particular, the least cost approach, as it is sometimes called, to climate stabilisation. You can actually achieve many global warming objectives at negative net cost.

Those are some of the things we know, and I imagine there are those of you in the audience who would argue with my category, but those are some of the things we know. What about the things that we know that we do not know?

(1) We know that we do not know how much warming will be experienced for a given increase in greenhouse gas concentrations? We do not really know that clearly yet.

(2) Exactly how the impacts of global warming will be experienced – globally, regionally and, most importantly of course, when?

(3) The sources and sinks of greenhouse gases are still not known exactly. We know something about them, but not nearly enough.

(4) The precise links between climate change and biological changes.

I would argue that these areas are not strictly areas of uncertainty since we know, on the whole, that we do not know these things. We move, in other words, into a third area which is governed by real uncertainty and this is the kind of uncertainty that I think we should all be worried about and which we might put our minds to and which we have barely started talking about. That is, we do not know the things that we do not know that we do not know.

We saw the IPCC model. The working groups were set up, there were scientific processes, there were impacts and there were responses. Implicit in that model and implicit in the way that the debate has been driven by scientists and by scientific information, valuable as that has been, is the notion of a linear progression from scientific process, to impacts, to responses. We know that the arrows do not all point that way. We know, in fact, that the relationship between the science, the impact and the responses is a very complex one.

Part of the problem is the paradigms that we use and the paradigms that we have come to depend upon for our policy formulation. I want to argue, in my presentation, that we need to go beyond, not to dispense with in any sense, but to go beyond current paradigms. If we are to address the wider challenge, not simply and as important as it is for government, industry and the private sector, but also for the population at large.

Most of the paradigms with which we are working, when we talk about global change, exclude as much as they include. They make flexible response difficult instead of easy. The make uncertainty a problem rather than a challenge.

Let us have a look at the way in which we approach environmental policy, in general, and I think this is true of global environmental change in particular. First of all, policy is based on the assumption that the closer to natural science, the social science becomes, particularly economics, the better. Social science, and particularly economics, has ground on more quantification, more measurement, more need for replicability and so on.

Of course, the very global warming problem reveals – one of the things it reveals – is that the natural sciences themselves increasingly deal with uncertainty. The more we know about the natural world, the less unlike ours it is in some respect. The quantum theory for example, if we look at subatomic particles, they are not things – they are processes we are looking at. Scientists have read the news on global warming, but scientists cannot take the necessary measures. They cannot move into the area of the human policy domain.

The limitations in what we know about nature are limitations in our understanding, not simply in the amount of facts we have. Knowledge tends to be measured and has been measured on this issue in terms of the aggregate data or the amount of information, rather than our understanding of what lies behind that data and how it is collected and what lies behind the business of making policy. All our policy models and frameworks, I would argue, are founded on underlying human commitments.

These underlying commitments are rarely explored. What do I mean by underlying commitments in this context?

– I mean things like the right to possess and use a motor car and to individualised motorised mobility.
– I mean the right to an increased standard of living.
– I mean the right to increase energy consumption if it is good business.
– I mean the right to regard the value of a product as the value at point of sale, rather than the value of the materials through a cycle over time.

Those are all underlying human commitments. They are not neutral. They are things that we have made and constructed. Neo classical economics, on the whole, starts as it were with a set of assumptions about those human commitments, without exploring them and without getting underneath them.

Neo classical economics see social interactions as instrumental, as designed to maximise utility, rather than constituting value in its own right. This is where the breadth of the debate about the environment in the future is revealed. Neo classical economics starts with a particular model of human behaviour which underpins it, and that model can best be represented as that of the rational individual calculator. We are looking at individuals, they are behaving rationally, and you are looking at their individual behaviour.

There are lots of problems with this model of a rational individual calculator. First of all it is ethnocentric. Which cultures does it apply to? Do we know that it applies to other cultures? Can we, with confidence, say that it applies to other cultures? The cultures do not begin south of Dover or Gibraltar. They start here in the midst of the developed countries. It is a highly ethnocentric kind of model. It is implying that this is the way we do things and the values we have are universal, which they are not.

Secondly, instead of a hypothesis, it is often treated as an axiom. It becomes an assumption of policy that people act as individuals and that they make a rational assessment of their interests, based on maximising utility. There is a good deal of evidence form the environmental debate, generally, that this is not the case. There is a great deal of public disquiet when this kind of language and discourse are used.

For example, in surveys, the term 'willingness to pay' has evoked a lot of problems. People using it in surveys have found that willingness to pay for environmental goods and services meets a lot of resistance. The language itself talks about the North Sea as a waste sink. The North Sea may be a waste sink to some people, to other people it is a livelihood if you are a fisherman, to other people its a place where, perish the thought, you go swimming. We talk in these terms, and I am suggesting to you that the language is implicit and is embedded in the way we think.

Thirdly, is the emphasis on the *individual* rational calculator. Society, groups of people in different forms, are not simply an aggregation of individuals. They are more than the paths of the individuals who make them up, what makes people behave in groups with certain interests in mind, and how do those groups and interests organise themselves to get their objectives? We are all part of different interests and groups and are out to try and in many cases, maintain the interests, although there may be a wider collective interest.

Looking at things in terms of individual decision making, in terms of the calculations that people make to maximise utility, I think is flawed. How do we know what people will do to reduce individual motorised mobility? How do we know what people will do to reduce energy consumption to assist recycling? Of course, we could introduce important policy measures, fiscal measures and others to try and influence behaviour and sometimes very effectively. That does not necessarily help advance the question of why people act as they do. In understanding that, and unlocking that box, we may be in a much more powerful position to influence the future of our planet.

The Gulf War, incidentally, I think is a good illustration of this because the ecology crisis which has received attention as a result of the Gulf War, has not been the ecology crisis we have all been talking about for the last two days. It has not been the dependence on fossil fuel resources in certain areas of the globe and the implications of that, among other things. It has been the effects of pollution and how important they are. That expresses some of the underlying commitments and assumptions in the debate.

I am asking how accurate are market signals of the whole gamut of environmental goods and services? We can refine them, we can make them better, but we need to step outside them. We need to look at cumulative social impacts. We need to see and investigate whether they are benign or malign. The telephone, the word processor, the internal combustion engine, nuclear power, pesticides, toxic chemicals, tobacco. I think if you list things like this then most of us have a way in which we automatically assume the benign environmental effect for one set of technologies of goods and the malign effect of others. These have never been systematically investigated, or in a very partial and limited way, in terms of the contribution that our dependence on these kinds of technologies and their use make to global environmental change in general.

Do we understand public attitudes to regulatory agencies, or to science? We have been talking about their importance, but we have not begun to investigate what the attitudes are to them and how it affects behaviour. Is the concern with environmental policy today evidence of public confidence in the ability of formal institutions, including governments? Is that what it represents? That is what a lot of politicians suggest that it does represent. Or is environmental policy debate like this one, evidence of a lack of confidence in current institutions and policies? It may be very interesting, it may be significant that so much of the debate about the environment are being conducted by NGOs, by private sector organisations outside the public state framework.

The title of my brief talk is 'a framework for survival' and you must be asking by now, when do we get on to that. What I am arguing is that we need to look back beyond the existing assumptions that we hold, beyond existing human commitments, and understand why we hold them and what alternatives might lie there. We need to admit, first of all, the possibility of plural rationalities, different routes to the truth. We are dealing, on the whole, with one kind of rationality, particularly in the case of new classical economics, important and powerful although it may be.

We need to examine our underlying human commitments. These underpin our models and our prejudices. We manage the globe and our resources as if our tastes, preferences, products and values are all, more or less, immutable. We really need to get down to what those tastes, preferences, products and value are all about.

Finally, we can see that what we do not know, we do not know, is governed by what we know. Our ability to access that area is concerned with what we do not know that we do not know. We cannot admit that we do not know it because of the paradigms and because of the way we approach the issues and that is governed precisely by what we know.

Moving beyond the current approach means being prepared to take a hard look at what we regard as fact, for our facts are often in one area an expression of our ignorance in another.

I would just like to explain that the ESRC's global environmental change programme certainly concerned some of these issues and is it concerned in a very large way with neo classical economics, and David Pearce is one of the Directors of the Centre which we are establishing between the University of East Anglia and University College in London – but it has a wider remit and more breadth than that. We are endeavouring to undertake in the next ten years, quite an ambitious programme of research which touches on various different areas. I will just very briefly outline them:

– Environmental change and public policy in Britain and the European Community generally, looking at a whole series of issues: energy options, agriculture and land use, scientific knowledge itself (which is where much of what I have been saying lies) and the relationship between industry, industrial sectors and clean technology development.

– International environmental policy and agreements concerned with the global commons, with international policy making and opinion formation, with technological transfer and the global environment.

– Regional case studies. In the first phase, we are going to look at three particular areas, critical zones outside the UK, topical forests, the arctic and sahel and sub-sahelian Africa. In the second phase, we will probably broaden that and include a concentration on water resources, population and on other critical zones.

So the idea of the ESRC's programme is to try and ensure that we insert the human dimensions of global change into the debate that is being conducted between scientists and politicians, to take social sciences into the heart, in a very policy relevant way, not a policy led way but a policy relevant way, into the heart of the global environmental change debate. Of course, at the same time, and this is part of my mission, to take the global environmental change debate into the heart of the social sciences.

QUESTIONS

(1) QUESTION: John Faulks
Centre for International
Environmental Law,
Clifford Chance, Solicitors

I have a comment to direct to Dr Vellinga. I was fortunate to attend the inter-governmental negotiating committee as part of the team of advisors to the Alliance of Small Island States and I have also experienced the New York marathon personally, so I do appreciate the comparison he made.

I would like his comment on whether he feels that the convention under negotiation will actually be effective to address the issues under discussion and whether the trialogue that he was suggesting will actually form the basis for that convention or whether the convention will stimulate the trialogue?

ANSWER: Dr Vellinga

My personal wish is that industry takes more initiative also in view of the negotiations. We do have an important meeting next month at the WICEM sponsored by the International Chamber of Commerce in Rotterdam where all international negotiations are talking with industry. In October, there is another important UNIDO meeting with industry. I hope there is an impetus from industry, or an impact of industry, on this negotiation process. I also think that we do need political leadership to make a negotiation successful – I mean successful in terms of a substantive convention. I am not sure whether that will happen. It will depend very much whether, within an OECD context, we can agree to certain emission targets or commitments. Once that breakthrough occurs, then I think we can make progress to a substantive negotiation. I hope that, within an OECD context, some preparations can be done which can be fed in the UN context because, in the end, you need the UN context.

(2) QUESTION : Ray Evans
Western Mining, Australia

One issue which I would like to bring up is the problem relating the political structures in our various countries.

In Australia and elsewhere in the western world, governments have to face elections from time to time, and the people that they appeal to for support are often very concerned about things like the standard of living and their tax burden. It seems to me that these considerations have been entirely absent from these discussions.

In Australia, we are now facing very subdued economic times. The environmentalists are now struggling in terms of trying to maintain public support for programmes and measures which will obviously reduce living standards even further. It seems to me that when you get down to the nitty gritty of political life throughout the western world, you are going to find the proposals which are going to reduce peoples' living standards quite significantly, such as massive transfers of income from poor people in rich countries to rich people in poor countries is going to lead to an electoral backlash.

ANSWER: Dr Redclift

Where I think I would put a question mark where you seem to be much more confident than I would be is in whether governments' constituencies really will assess the matter simply in terms of cost, and we have seen this morning that it can be demonstrated that many environmental measures actually have net benefits. As consumers, and as individuals, very often I think the public is ahead of governments, very much, and so I think the issue is much more 'are governments willing to act' than it is 'can governments afford to act given that their constituents would not back them up.'

I think we see a lot of evidence today, at least on the part of consumers, that people would like very much more to behave and to act in an environment friendly way. What you are suggesting is something that we do not really know yet. This happened, in a sense, in the Netherlands recently that very few governments have actually gone to their electorate with a package of environmental policy measures and said 'what do you think of this?

I think that there is evidence that governments have been pushed into greener policies by their constituencies. I am not saying there is not a cost there, attached to that, so I am not as sure as you are that it is bad politics for governments to do this.

COMMENT: Dr Vellinga

Of course, the undercurrent is not driven by politics. The IPCC Scientific Report was not influenced by politics. The industrial commitment we now see occurring in the Netherlands are not really driven by politics, they are also driven by a genuine concern of the industrial sector to survive over the next ten to twenty years. They are sensitive to the public as well and when the public gets more interested in environmental friendly goods and services, then industry should respond one way or another. I think there is an undercurrent and, of course, you may have backlashes politically every now and then.

(3) QUESTION: Dr Pearlman

This is for Mr Vellinga regarding the Phase 1 and Phase 2. On Phase 2 you said reductions of emissions by the industrialised countries, would include a comprehensive approach. I did not notice a reference to the comprehensive approach under Phase 1 and I am wondering if that was intentional?

ANSWER: Dr Vellinga

It was not intentional. I said there is stabilisation of all greenhouse gas emissions. I pointed out, that one controversial issue is comprehensive approach or gas by gas approach and I purposely put an 'and/or' and I think and I hope that the process of negotiations will end up with a kind of mixture on the comprehensive approach as an umbrella for the greenhouse gases and see where we can end up with at least some commitments on gases as well – like we have on CFCs. You might find ways, perhaps with margins on other gases. Setting a total cap and see within the cap what you can do on individual gases.

QUESTION: Dr Pearlman

Would that apply to Phase 1 as well, so when you spoke of stabilisation of emissions by industrialised nations, under Phase 1, you would have both stabilisation on a comprehensive approach and then see whether you could get specific agreements for stabilisation of individual gases or not?

ANSWER: Dr Vellinga

You put me on very thin ice now, but the position of the European countries and EFTA countries is if it will be a substantive convention in Brazil, then the minimum requirement would be to have stabilisation of CO_2 emissions in industrialised countries.

QUESTION: Dr Pearlman

I was speaking in terms of *your* proposal of course.

ANSWER: Dr Vellinga

As I said, maybe you could allow for some margins under the umbrella of the comprehensive approach, but that is just trying to look for ways to bridge the gap between OECD countries. Politically, the EEC position and EFTA position I think will very fiercely ask from the US also to take this political intent, maybe on a pledge and review basis, for stabilising CO_2 emissions at 1990 levels.

14

INTERNATIONAL, NATIONAL AND REGIONAL LEGAL FRAMEWORKS: A NEW CONCEPT IN INTERNATIONAL LAW

Malcolm Forster

Freshfields

What I want to do is really just put down three or four little markers. Firstly, what used to be a heresy but is becoming less so, I will attempt to establish briefly that the veneration of the Montreal Protocol process is a dangerous delusion. Then I will pass on to the suggestion, that we will dismiss almost out of hand that what we need, therefore, is a much more fundamental review of international law principles because we are certainly not going to get that. We shall then look briefly at what possible advances we can make using the system in which the international law was made at the moment, a little bit about looking for existing mechanisms. Finally, some suggested way forwards.

Montreal Protocol Process

I do not seek to deny that the Montreal Protocol process, as it has started and has continued, represents something of a watershed in the way in which these matter are regulated. But, if I may, I would just like to caution a little of care because there were a number of factors which apply to the success of the Montreal Protocol process so far as it has been a success which do not apply, on the whole, at least to many of the greenhouse gases. Although many of the factors which contributed to this success do apply there are significant differences.

Features of the Montreal Protocol process which made a substantial contribution to its success included; a fairly narrow group of targets, a group of substances which, for the most part were of industrial application. Many of which formed an element of a sort of recognisable group of industrial processes and, in many cases anyway, the trade patterns in them were somewhat transparent. The use of many of those substances were localised at least in the sense that they were used in installations which, to some extent, were already subject to existing institutional controls from the environmental point of view.

The sector point of view concentrated also in industries, for the most, in industrialised countries fairly well sensitised to environmental concerns or in the most highly industrialised sectors of industrialising countries. The results of that, effectively, were that those who were engaged in the useful treatment of those substances were already familiar with the business of dealing with governments and dealing with demands imposed upon them by the international community and skilled, to some extent, in responding to those demands when they came.

In addition, many of the industries were capable of making their views readily appreciated in government circles, not always but usually, through already existing trade association and so on, capable of organising at least at national and usually regional or possibly even at international level. Those industries frequently also had not only financial, but institutional capability to perceive the need for substitution or for changes in the way in which they employ target substances which were foreseeable as a result of this process and the financial capacity to respond.

Global Warming: The Debate
Edited by Peter Thompson with the assistance of John P. O'Hara
© 1991 Strategy Europe Ltd. Published 1991 by John Wiley & Sons Ltd

Finally, and perhaps most importantly of all, the substitution of the substances dealt with under the Montreal Protocol process hiterhto, or indeed under some of the other international conventions on the subject, required changes only of a technical or financial nature, but not necessarily including social or cultural changes – at least not to any marked degree.

It seems to me that, when we go and look at the greenhouse gases, we meet a number of very different circumstances with which it is, by no means, clear that the international legal framework is competent to deal, at least at the moment. Production is not confined to industrialised countries or even to the industrialised sector of other countries, the first time perhaps that the international legal community has had to deal with the problem of developing countries as macro polluters on the global scale. We all know, of course, there is chronic local pollution in developing countries. On the whole, we have not hitherto thought of them as major polluters on the global scale.

Production is not confined to industrial sectors, but much more widely spread, including transport, the domestic as well – heating, cooking and so on. Even in a country like this, substantial contributions of CO_2 are made from the domestic sector and much higher, of course, in some developing countries.

This diffuseness of distribution of, as it were, polluting sources makes it difficult to produce a significant institutional counterpart to the international community in negotiation or implementation and, not only is the scale of response investment probably larger, but the remedies which are called upon are not simply limited to investment that may require substantial social and cultural change.

If that is the case, then it may well be that the Montreal process, the picking off as it were of gases one by one, which we have referred to, may not produce the sort of results which one looks for. On the other hand, one is glad to see increasing evidence of the abandonment of the proposal to produce a sort of law of the sea type of result for law of the atmosphere. It is very sad for those of us involved in the law of the sea, it was jolly good fun roaming around in Geneva and New York and Caracas and that sort of thing. Everybody had a jolly good time, but it is now unusual to see as, only a couple of years ago,

I heard a very distinguished expert (who I will not name) who said the following:-

"A substantial number of articles of the Law of the Sea Convention can be incorporated into a Law of the Atmosphere Convention simply by replacing the words 'marine environment' with the words 'atmospheric environment'."

It seems to me that that is really a very dangerous approach. The Law of the Sea Convention is subject to a lot of misapprehension, as you know. For example, most of it is not in force – some of it is through the customary international law in my view – but those parts which have achieved success, have achieved success because they had a substantial pre-existing element of agreement amongst civilised countries which could be represented, therefore, as a codification of that practice. That is certainly the case in terms of atmospheric questions or, if it is, only at a level of such generality as not really to take the matter forward very much further by a conventional route.

Ideally, the case would be the creation of a much more fundamental review of some of the principles of international law by which the international natural resource laws set its compasses for some years. The doctrine of permanent sovereignty over natural resources, for example, which is almost a holy tenet of developed countries is, of course, wholly pernicious in this context, as indeed the doctrine of sovereignty itself is a much more essential building block of the international order but there is some evidence I suppose, of some erosion. A new De Jure Gentium of the environment is unlikely as a result of the Brazil conference, much though one would like to think otherwise.

There are possibilities, it seems to me in the existing process, of which we see elements in the kind of negotiations which Dr Vellinga has described. The international community is becoming infinitely more sophisticated in the way in which it reacts to these kinds of pressures. For example, the role of conventions, agreements and protocols are becoming a little different. It has been recognised that they are no longer as suitable as they were once thought to environmental factors which require precision, but the ability to rapidly change those precise provisions.

We have also seen, in many of the existing conventions and international obligations, an increasing willingness to think in a rather more sophisticated manner, a rather more complex manner about the obligations to which we subject our countries. We no longer, for example, assume that in international law, as in national law, equality is equity. One sees increasingly the acceptance amongst states of the imposition of differing obligations between the parties, even in the long range air pollution treaty, we have seen that. The two speed convention which is much criticised in respect of sulphur dioxide, for example. This is not, incidentally in my view, necessarily a bad thing. Half a loaf is better than no bread and so on.

Within the European Community, the large combustion plants directive has a much more sophisticated level of tailoring the requirements of the directive to the member states to which it is subject. Presumably, we will look to see, in industrialised countries, much more of this with the adoption of critical loads approach to atmospheric pollution controls. It may well be that a factor of the ozone layer process which will be extremely important in the context we are now considering, also displays this inequality of treatment, by which I mean the selective incentives which are offered in the ozone process both to developing countries, as is well know, but also the sort of grandfathering provisions in respect of facilities in production when the first draft is negotiated.

We have heard from Dr Vellinga of the importance of regionalisation in the negotiation. The regionalisation, it appears to me, may well have a considerable contribution to make in terms of implementation as well. We have learned from other areas of international environmental law that it is much easier to achieve a certain degree of collaboration between states which share a certain common history, perhaps a certain common culture, and perhaps a certain common level of economic development.

In addition, it seems that the way in which the international community has responded, at least in the environmental field, to the sort of built in obsolescence of international agreements, may well also play a role in the area we are looking at. In particular, perhaps, in the area of provisional application of treaties which, in formal terms anyway, are not actually binding as a matter of international law.

If that were to be the case, however, it seems that one has perhaps to ask oneself what are the first series of targets? What are the first things one should set out to achieve with this more flexible, but on the whole, probably traditional approach to international environmental law making? We have heard from Dr Vellinga the dispute, or difference of opinion, between the necessity to advance on a comprehensive global approach or to go on with the gas by gas basis. It seems to me that it may well be that there is some value in considering the gas by gas basis, if only that it seems to me on principle it is probably easier to apply these kinds of mechanisms to that approach – if one is looking, as it were, for specific obligations implemented, or at least partially implemented fairly quickly.

It may well be, however, that what international lawyers really ought to be doing is to be concentrating not so much on that question, which perhaps we should simply allow the international diplomatic and political community to decide for us and then try and implement it as best we can. What the international lawyers may be able to do, in the interim, is to consider those matters which were referred to by Dr Vellinga as part of the working group 3 agenda. Perhaps we should be looking to see whether there is in not only the international environmental law, but elsewhere, some model to enable us to begin to prepare for functional advancement on the international level. Perhaps our most important contribution might be to try and produce some kind of improved efficiency in the international regulation of matters such as compliance, assessment of dealing with scientific co-operation in a genuinely efficient sense of working with these old chestnuts of financial assistance and transfer technology.

These matters perhaps are those on which international lawyers might be wise to set their sights. I do not think, that is lowering their sights necessarily, these are matter on which, you can make a case for saying that lawyers ought to have some degree of special knowledge and we ought really to be able to deliver the goods. If we were to do that, it may be that we may help our colleagues in other disciplines in falling into another trap.

QUESTIONS

(1) QUESTION: Sonia Christiansen,
                        University of Sussex

I think it is true and I have written that the environmental outcome of the law of the sea negotiations, in the end, was very little else but the codification of practice on marine pollution. However, because the negotiations took so long, a great deal of this practice actually took place during the negotiations. There may be something to be learned for the air pollution thing if we do not rush too much, if we build in a lot of flexibility and encourage industry and regional groups, in particular countries, to make their separate agreements, to gain experience and also take into account the different problems. For instance, you might get again at what you might call a dual track development. Under the umbrella of the global warming, a very flexible and probably repeatedly reviewed progress at the global level, you will give a chance to particular industry such as the coal industry or the car industry to make their own liability (which is not the right word here I know), but you might give agreements towards certain targets.

If this goes along side, but slightly tied, I think you will get a very invigorating perhaps and mutually interacting process of negotiations at several levels. It would also bring in the idea of learning over time and of not putting too many people into one room, and too many countries into one room all the time. I think then the negotiations become almost impossible. So do not knock the Law of the Sea Conference, partly because of what you mentioned, and because I have put a lot of effort into this.

I have also spent the last five years on international air pollution and European air pollution. You can learn from this and I am terribly impressed by what mankind has actually been able to achieve and what industries have been able to achieve.

ANSWER: Malcolm Forster

Please do not misunderstand me, I do not describe the Law of the Sea Convention as entirely negative, but quite the opposite. You are quite right that the contribution of talking about the doctrine develops a doctrine. Of course it does and, apart from anything else, it simply makes the ideas which originally seem terribly shocking and rather frightening, rather less threatening by the time you have spent ten years talking about them. I think my warning was really against, what I think is now, in most circles anyway, really a danger which has been by-passed – the 'quick-fix' blockbuster convention approach. The Law of the Sea Convention's beneficial effect is infinitely more complex and sophisticated than that.

Part V

The Economic Debate

15

THE ECONOMIC IMPLICATIONS OF GLOBAL WARMING

Nicholas J. Hartley

Head of UK Department of the Environment's
Environment Protection Economics Division

Why worry about change? Economists have always stressed that economies which work through free markets are likely to be pretty adaptable. Remember, for instance, the economists' input into the 1970s' 'limits to growth' debate. Thus, while Thomas Carlyle called economics 'the dismal science', the role of economics in the global warming debate has tended to be rather a jolly one. Amidst the dire warnings of the scientists the message of some of the economics profession has been 'don't worry, be happy'.

This is not my message today. I shall try to explain how, in my view, economists should view the choice. Our foundation stone is the report of the IPCC. The overall conclusion that the man made increase in greenhouse gas concentrations has proceeded at a rate far faster than anything previously seen in the past ten thousand years, is indisputable – and must provide the starting point for all our efforts.

However, the scientific analysis of the problem is still unfolding. It will be central to much of what I have to say this morning that policy makers faced by the continuing, albeit slowly narrowing, uncertainty of the scientists' projections are inevitably going to have to take a complicated set of decisions weighing the possible ranges of costs and benefits, and the risks of different courses of action.

IPCC suggests that there is now widespread agreement that the best guess of the current rate of climate change is that world temperatures are projected to increase by between 0.2°C and 0.5°C per decade. That is two to five times the rate of change that occurs naturally in fluctuations taking place over thirty to fifty year periods. The range largely reflects uncertainty about how we should account for changes in cloud cover as the earth warms.

We are told that the world is 0.4° warmer than it was in the 1860s. However, computer models of the climate suggest that we should expect natural fluctuation of plus or minus 0.5° centigrade and so we are advised that warming is within the observed variation. Given the models, I am told that it is not until perhaps the year 2000 that the warming signal will show through the natural variation.

We have much less confidence in the regional predictions, particularly for countries like the UK where we have poor understanding of the response of the oceans to changes in temperature. A better understanding of this may take at least ten to fifteen years to resolve. Thus, although one obvious reaction to warming is to try to adapt climate change, the uncertainties about the effects of climate change are such that only in a few cases could a clear path of adaptation now be mapped out.

The choices we now face are difficult, but they are susceptible to analysis. We need to know the balance of risks, the timescale over which the uncertainties will be resolved, the flexibility with which changes could be made, and the costs of making changes both now and in the future.

Economists naturally think within a cost benefit framework. Thus, if the costs which would be associated with the adaptation to climate change – the benefits – exceed the value of the resources

Global Warming: The Debate
Edited by Peter Thompson with the assistance of John P. O'Hara
© 1991 Strategy Europe Ltd. Published 1991 by John Wiley & Sons Ltd

expended to avoid the change – the costs – then the expenditure would seem worthwhile. On the basis of this comparison, nations could choose either to adapt their economies to cope with new climatic conditions, or to spend resources now to avoid the climate change which is forecast on the basis of unchanged policies.

Most probably, some combination of the two will be appropriate, if only because some climate change is irreversible as a result of past actions. But, I am afraid, this is not and never will be a precise calculus. Finally, it is a matter for political judgement.

There are people who suggest that, for parts of the developed world and indeed even parts of the developing world, the overall impact of climate change will probably be of minor importance so it will be better to adapt than to avoid. Quite a lot turns precisely how the climate change is specified. Any tendency for world temperature to increase by more than $0.1°C$ to $0.2°C$ per decade, would move us irreversibly into an area where we are unsure of what will happen. What Professor David Pearce has called the 'zone of potential surprise'.

The term 'global warming' encompasses a range of different climatic changes. Some regions will get warmer, some will get drier, some will get wetter – as Dr Houghton has told us. More important, perhaps, there is the prospect of significant changes in the pattern of the world's weather and, indeed, in the underlying determinants of the world's weather, like the various ocean currents. My scientific colleagues advise me that models of these sort of effects are only now just becoming available. At the moment, it is not possible to make firm predictions of the way in which different regions will be affected by the various aspects of weather – rain, storms, hurricanes, drought. There is considerable uncertainty about the scale and magnitude of these changes, but there is a non-negligible chance that, in some parts of the world, these changes will seem to be catastrophic.

In the face of the uncertainty and the potential irreversibility of the changes, should nations continue to be risk neutral? That is, be indifferent between equal risks of good and bad outcomes. I think not. Some of the climate change catastrophes are so severe that far greater weight should be placed on avoiding them than on the possibility of a favourable outcome. In other words, given the possibilities for chaos, most people and most societies are like to be risk averse.

There is no Galactic Insurance plc for whom we can pay a premium to cover against this risk, but there are still two different ways of approaching it:

(1) To invest to reduce the likelihood of disaster which means accepting some costs now for a reduced future risk.

(2) The opposite, is to decide that if the uncertainty is about to be removed, and there is a good chance that scientists stand to get a much better handle on the problem in the years to come, we should wait to see how the uncertainty resolves itself before coming to a judgement.

Prevarication is always tempting and it is low cost if you are lucky. It is right that we should consider how far to scale down any initial response to the problem because of the likelihood that firmer scientific evidence will be forthcoming reasonably soon. This approach, however, also presents problems. The possible danger increases the longer the wait, and the present risk is greater than it seemed at first. The thermal inertia of the oceans means that the observed temperature rise always lags behind the greenhouse gas concentration. Thus, even if we could magically freeze the concentration of greenhouse gases when the climate got too warm, warming will continue to increase for some time on the basis of effects which were already in the pipeline. It may already be too late to sit back and hope for the best. A sensible assessment of the odds points to making some investment now.

It is as well to recognise that there are three parallel ways to invest to lessen the global climate risks to future generations:

(1) We can intensify the amount of scientific research as a means of reducing climate and impact uncertainties.

(2) We can foster the research and development of new supply and conservation technologies as a means of reducing abatement costs.

(3) We can make immediate reductions in emissions.

The likely returns to further scientific research to reduce climate related uncertainties are very great indeed. If the uncertainties can be reduced, then we can know with much greater certainty what the right path to take is and we can avoid expensive mistakes.

Indeed, there are important inter-relationships between the choices which we can make in order to protect ourselves from the effects of climate changes, and the patterns of scientific research. Where adaptation to a new climate is easy then it can be argued that there is less need to chase down the scientific uncertainties. However, where the time lags and costs involved in adapting to climate change are long, then the pay-offs to greater scientific understanding can be very large.

I want to consider the assessments which have been of the likely cost of the damage resulting from climate change. We must first agree on the focus of our interest. Are we interested in the world as a whole, or just in the welfare of our own nation states? The problem is a global one. It seems to me that a global focus is essential. It is pretty certain, I think, that there are some nation states which are likely to lose substantially from even quite minor global warming. Indeed, it may be that their fate has already been sealed. The potential adverse effects include loss of infrastructure, disruption to agriculture, famine and disease, and enforced migration.

The other side of this coin is that if only modest global warming was to result, there may even be some states which stand to gain. Certainly there must be some regions in the world which are better off as a result. Each nation is going to want to undertake its own calculus but, as I say, I also think that some world view is needed.

One point about a worldwide calculus is that there is no necessary reason to accept the decision rules that the sum of the costs and benefits need to add up to zero, so the gains to the gainers are fully matched by the losses to the losers. It is essential to the business of political choice that decision makers have to make a judgement about the right balance between the impacts on different communities. It is perfectly possible that they may put a very high weight on the losses attaching to particular people, so that these cannot be wholly off-set by equivalent gains elsewhere. These sort of distributional issues will inevitably lie behind the political judgements which governments will make when negotiating about a greenhouse gas framework convention.

In any case, a narrow calculus is I suggest misleading. The UK would not be isolated from the world economy and high damage costs elsewhere in the world could lead to difficult to predict costs for the UK – for example, greater pressures for immigration from, or income support to, developing countries. Adaptation of the UK industry to changing patterns of world trade and the consequences of political instability and conflicts elsewhere. Even if the UK could remain immune, we might even so wish to assist adaptation elsewhere by increasing our help to countries which could be very seriously damaged by global warming, many of which have close links with the UK.

Let us look more precisely at the likely damages. Attempts to estimate defensive costs in various parts of the economy are at an early stage, and it is an extremely difficult exercise. We do not generally have separate estimates of the costs of adapting to different levels of climate change, which is what we really want. One way in which the costs are being estimated is that researchers try to identify those parts of the economy which seem to be most dependent upon the weather. They generally conclude that only a small part of the economy, that is of any advanced industrial economy, is now dependent on weather. For example, Professor William Nordhaus estimates that, for the USA, this is at most 15%.

We know, of course, that the possibility of sea level rise will have catastrophic effects on those areas where populations live in low-lying land. Estimates have been made of the costs of constructing sea defences to defend low-lying areas against rising seas. For the world as a whole, these total hundreds of billions of dollars, though they are not large as a proportion of GDP. This expenditure would, moreover, be spread over several decades. Even so it may not be sufficient to save some of the most vulnerable areas.

In the UK, estimates of expenditure on coastal defences start at £5 billion, broadly in line with the expenditure needed in most other equivalent nations, but this expenditure again would be spread over several decades. The likelihood of increase frequency of major storms is not known, but the impact could be substantial. We, in the UK, started to see some of the possibilities of catastrophe in the great storms of 1987 and 1989. I make no claims that these storms were as a result of global warming, but they are precisely the kind of impacts which we would have to anticipate as a result of climate change.

I would like to be able to put some monetary value on these possibilities of chaos and catastrophe. The insurance claims resulting from the 1987 storm topped £1 billion. There is also an estimate that increased hurricane damage in the USA could cost up to $750 million a year, but I should warn you that one of the tricks of this game on both sides is to throw large numbers about. I shall try to be honest and put the numbers into perspective: £1 billion is in fact only 0.2% of the UK's annual GDP. It is, therefore, in itself not a large number but the numbers like this may magnify if more than one effect is found.

Moreover, I would suggest very strongly, and I think this is an important point, that the damage costs derived from insurance claims underestimate the welfare losses attaching to the damage from wild weather. Again, consider the 1987 storm: I suggest that a number of us would have paid a considerable amount of money to have avoided the damage, to have avoided the upset to existing ways of life and to existing landscapes and, therefore, to have resisted the unsought change. If we could get estimates of this value by asking people what they would be willing to pay to avoid catastrophes, then I suggest that we might end up with much larger numbers than we are currently being presented with.

One part of the economy which is obviously dependent upon the weather is agriculture. Here there have been suggestions that initially, at least, increases in CO_2 will aid agricultural productivity in some sectors and climates. I understand there is something in this, though I do not think this effect continues ad infinitum and there comes a point when increased concentrations of CO_2 and the associated changes in weather are likely to become increasingly damaging to agricultural production.

Nevertheless, for a while, there seemed not too much to worry about, at least in the UK where the agricultural sector is, in any case, pretty flexible. However, higher world temperatures will produce large shifts in the structure and distribution of world agriculture and forecasts show a range of possible costs from a very low total adjustment cost, to an increase in the resource costs of producing the world's agricultural needs of about 10%, which implies a cost equivalent to 0.5% of the world's GDP. With larger costs, the faster the required rate of adjustment.

In the UK, some parts of the economy would almost certainly make some gains from the predicted changes in winter climate. The construction and transport industries are obvious examples. Manufacturing is likely to be able to adapt, though this need not be the case everywhere in the world. Professor Nordhaus believes that, in the USA, most of the new manufacturing and service economy can make itself pretty independent of climatic conditions. I suppose it is true that, so long as firms can get access to supplies of water, if necessary brought from some distance, and if their premises can be air conditioned, then they can effectively be isolated from the exterior environment. However, I note from a recent report in the Financial Times that the Californian economy is coming under severe strains as a result of a shortage of water and that one area in particular, which it may hit, is the production of micro-chips which depend upon a large supply of water in order to wash the finished products. I am not therefore quite so sure that the existing economies are quite as independent of the weather as Professor Nordhaus suggests.

Nevertheless, if there are costs, they are mostly of a transitional nature. We may have a current economy which is more dependent on and adapted to the weather than some people think but, clearly, over a period of twenty, thirty or fifty years marked changes in the economy are going to take place. Consider the rapid changes in the UK economy just in the last decade. In this case, if the change can be taken slowly, then there is very little obvious industrial cost of shutting down facilities in one part of the country and starting them up in another in order to adjust to a new pattern of climate.

To conclude this part of the argument, I agree with those economists who have doubts about the scale of the problem, that it is wrong simply to impose judgements about the likely scale of climate change on the present structure of economic and social activity. I do not find this quite such an overwhelming argument as they do. I am pretty certain that there are strong desires to maintain existing patterns of community and settlement which should, I believe, be taken into account when it comes to making judgements about the scale of the costs which is worth bearing in order to control the rate of change of climate.

Moreover, it is not necessarily the case that the economy will be adjusting to meet a new equilibrium. Climate change would likely be continuing and possibly subject to some sharp discontinuities, what we might call surprises.

We generally have much better assessments of the costs of reducing greenhouse gas emissions than of living with climate change. I turn now to this part of the argument.

Everything suggests that, if we are to make changes in the short run, we will want to do this in the most efficient way. That is, we would want to chose ways of reducing emissions which have minimal cost. Ideally, we want to chose ways which have no cost. Indeed, which have an overall net benefit. How likely is this? I am not going to go through all the listed measures with you. There are some 'no regrets' measures – I am sure of that. For example, there are some market imperfections which are stopping people from doing sensible things at the moment and, if these can be removed, then we can get changes in energy use which will benefit everybody. Greenhouse gas emissions will be reduced, domestic and industrial costs of energy use will be reduced, and the economy as a whole would benefit.

Equally, some existing policies which are being pursued for other very good reasons will have spin-off effects which are beneficial to the output of greenhouse gases. The obvious example is the reductions we are making in the reduction of CFCs. Another example is that of the reductions which we, in the UK, are making in emissions of acidic gases. These reductions are likely to have a net effect which is beneficial, not only on acid rain, but also on greenhouse gas emissions. I am sure, therefore, that while there is still uncertainty about the magnitude and the cost of climate change, any sensible government will look first to 'no regrets' policies.

However, fairly soon, reductions of this kind are not likely to take us far enough. In this case, we would be looking to go beyond 'no regrets' measures and looking towards the possibility of making more costly changes in our economic systems in order to reduce greenhouse gas emissions. We should look first to changes which could be reversed fairly easily later, that is when the scientific evidence solves some of the present uncertainties.

But, let us assume that today's insurance is fully justified, that long term reductions in emission are needed. Where then are the costs associated with a more frugal use of energy? It is true that in some cases, as I said, people are wasting resources because the market which serves them are imperfect or there are failures to provide them with the right information. In other cases, however, people are being perfectly sensible in avoiding new investments. It may be that it really is very costly to organise yourself or your firm to reduce the use of energy. Moreover, economists would be at pains to stress that measures which would interfere with consumer choice generally have a cost and often a large one.

Estimates of costs depend, in part, on the scale of the reduction which is required. With big reductions in emissions, particularly CO_2 emissions, major changes in lifestyle are being required. Existing investments would be wasted. Major new investments in infrastructure would be needed and all that would be very costly. These may mainly be dislocation costs, that is the costs from moving from one structure of industry to another, one-off not continuing costs, but there are no less serious for that. Moreover, there are likely to be some continuing costs attaching to policies to reduce greenhouse gas emissions. These, however, are in my view very difficult to derive and estimate.

As I said when I began, economies are very flexible. However, we cannot know quite how long run technical change would adapt to a world where energy was much more expensive. I need not remind you just how fundamental the use of energy is to our economic system and how wide ranging the changes must be if we are to reduce energy use and, therefore, CO_2 emissions. Thus, given that world economies are well adapted to the existing structure of relative prices it is hard not to envisage some continuing cost, at least as far as it is sensible to make economic projections.

The high cost of controlling greenhouse gas emissions suggests the need for cost effective measures, both nationally and internationally. Take national measures first. There is a growing belief that a market based solution, giving producers and consumers some choice about the way in which to meet a given target it to be preferred so far as possible. In effect this means working through the price mechanism. Nevertheless, an alternative, the regulatory route like standards of energy efficiency or even the banning of certain products, has its role especially in the early stages while we are looking for 'no regrets' measures.

What is good nationally, can be even better internationally. If it is so many times cheaper to make reductions in CO_2 emissions in the energy inefficient countries, in Eastern Europe, than in the OECD countries then it is better to make the biggest reductions there. The other example which is often mentioned is that of measures to encourage afforestation as a means of creating carbon sinks.

How can this efficiency be achieved? In principle, schemes of compensation could be provided so that gainers compensated losers and, so long as the world as a whole gained, there would be a good case for the policy. In practice, there must be doubts as to how far adequate compensation schemes can be devised, though the schemes for internationally tradeable targets are, in principle, one such scheme.

Let me summarise the potential role of economists and economic thinking in the global warming debate. In the first place, economists' cost benefits techniques and approaches can help policy makers to weigh up the difficult choices between doing nothing and adapting to change, and doing something in reducing emissions or investing in carbon sinks, but no analysis is complete which fails to recognise the current uncertainties about the final effect of what is now happening. All of use should be in some awe of the implications of the world's entering the zone of potential surprise. A risk averse strategy would, in part, consist of continued investment in the scientific research which will help to narrow the current uncertainties. It would also consist in the adoption of 'no regrets' measures to reduce emissions.

But it is also likely to see the purchase of some insurance, the adoption of some measures which, although they are costly, would be justified should the worst predictions of the scientists prove to be well founded. Such measures should themselves ideally be reversible should they be proved to be unnecessary later. In most countries, analysts are now working within this sort of framework. As yet, however, too few of the analytical boxes have been completed. There is, I am afraid, the need for a lot more empirical work.

16

CAN EASTERN EUROPE COPE WITH TARGETS SET BY THE WEST?

Professor Zdzislaw Kaczmarek

Leader, Water Resources Project, IIASA
(International Institute for Applied Systems Analysis)
Formerly Chairman of the Polish State Council for Environmental Protection
and Secretary General of the Polish Academy of Sciences

I have been asked to talk on the Eastern European situation and, in particular, I will try to answer the question – can Eastern Europe cope with the targets set by the west? This question has been asked in the context of global warming.

I would like to organise my talk around four topics:

(1) What are the targets set by the Western developed countries?

(2) Should the emissions be stabilised in the coming years?

(3) Should it decrease?

(4) How much?

The answer is not at all easy, clear or simple. At the 1988 Toronto Conference on Changing Environment, it was agreed that at least 20% reduction of CO_2 emissions, before the years 2005, is necessary as the first step to stabilise the situation. But it was clear for the highly industrialised countries that reduction of emissions should be much higher in order to attain sufficient containment of greenhouse effect.

However, the Ministerial Conference in Nordwig on Atmospheric Pollution and Climatic change, was much more cautious saying in its declaration that it orders all industrialised countries to support the process of IPCC through the investigation of the feasibility of achieving targets to limit or reduce CO_2 emissions, including for example 20% reduction as recommended by the Scientific World Conference on Changing Atmosphere in Toronto in 1988.

This statement has been supported by the Ministerial Declaration of the second World Climate Conference in Geneva where we may read that the conference urges all developed countries to establish targets or national programmes or strategies which will have significant effect on limiting emissions and that the conference acknowledges that those developed countries with yet relatively low energy consumption or some with economies in transition should establish targets which accommodate social economic growth.

What happened after the first World Climate Conference in 1979? What happened with the CO_2 emissions? We may see that in the last ten years, the global emissions increased about 16% and the only region where we really see some decrease of emission is Western Europe. In all the other regions, we have either stabilisation or some increase.

Emissions in Eastern European countries seemed to be stabilised during this decade. Although reliable data are not yet available for the last two years, 1989 to 1990, I think there is a high probability that because of some recession in this region, the energy consumption and consequently the greenhouse

Global Warming: The Debate
Edited by Peter Thompson with the assistance of John P. O'Hara
© 1991 Strategy Europe Ltd. Published 1991 by John Wiley & Sons Ltd

gases emissions has dropped by about 10% in relation to 1988.

We all know what are the possible measures to reduce energy related radiatively active trace gases. Usually the following four approaches are identified:

(1) Reduction by means of energy conservation.

(2) Reduction by fossil fuel substitutions.

(3) Reduction by means of nuclear energy, but I would like to mention that the use of nuclear energy is being questioned now in many countries, including Eastern Europe.

(4) Reduction by means of renewable energy sources which, at present, are of very limited use in Eastern Europe. For example, in Poland less than 2% of all energy production is based on hydropower and other non-fossil fuels.

For the Eastern European countries, I think the energy conservation seems to be the most promising in the coming decade. The difference between Western parts of Europe and the Eastern parts of Europe is very evident here. The use in Eastern Europe is about six times more energy for a unit of gross national product.

The next question I would like to address is global warming, the main environmental issue in Eastern Europe? My answer to this question is definitely no. Central and Eastern European countries, despite diverse climatic, economic and natural conditions, suffer from many common environmental problems. Pollution of air, water and soil occurs in many locations throughout the region. Inhabitants of cities are frequently exposed to extremely dangerous levels of pollutants emitted by industry, by transportation and from other sources.

Higher than the European average occurrence of birth defects, learning disabilities, some kinds of diseases, shorter lifespans and other effects have been reported in some heavily contaminated areas in Eastern Europe. So, the major environmental problems in this part of Europe are rooted in the socio-economic structure of these countries and these structures' major characteristics have included unrealistic pricing, inefficient industries, non-enforcement of environmental laws and, to some extent, indifference to environmental problems by industry, by state authorities but also, to some extent, by the general public. Currently, also institutional structures for environmental management are inadequate.

What are the near term priorities for corrective actions in East and Central Europe? I think that sweeping economic reform is a prerequisite for successful environmental protection. Key elements of required economic reforms include privatisation pricing of natural resources and energy, the structuring and modernising of industry, and eliminating high state subsidies of industry and agriculture. If economic reform occurs slowly or not at all in these countries, then the quality of the environment in the region will continue to deteriorate with all these consequences.

The existing environment management system of countries of the Eastern European region needs to be reviewed, changed, and new national environment management system should be based on integrated environment management which promotes the comprehensive management of hazards in air, water and land in order that such hazards may be reduced.

According to our calculations, the restoration of environment will cost Eastern Europe hundreds of billions of dollars and per capita GNP in these countries is, as we all know, three to five times lower than in the West. So one frequently may hear the question – will the East Europeans be willing to pay for the clean up? This questions assumes, of course that the clean up will trade off between so-called 'green' environment and other needs – housing, food etc, not to mention capital needed for economic restructuring.

Taking into account the general bad shape of Eastern European economies and an urgent need to improve the quality of environmental resources, we have to come to the conclusion that the long term threats like global warming and its possible consequences are, at present, rather low on the political agenda. The reasons are obvious:

(1) Other needs are more pressing and more urgent

(2) There are still a lot of uncertainties with the climate change issue.

The problem of the 'no regrets' policy has already been mentioned by the previous speaker. In accordance with the conclusions of the IPCC Working Group on Response Strategies, the most effective and rational actions are those which are beneficial for reasons other than climate change and justifiable in their own right, for example increased energy efficiency and lower greenhouse gas emission technologies, better management of forests, other national resources, reductions in emissions of CFCs and so on. Secondly we should use economically efficient and cost effective measures, in particular those that use market base mechanisms. Then measures able to serve multiple social, economic and environmental purposes. Tools and methods should be flexible so that they can be easily modified to respond to increased understanding of scientific technological and economic aspects of climate change.

In his speech in February 1990, the US Secretary of State said that if the results of international scientific research demonstrates that climatic conditions will not change in a significant way, we will have no regrets for such actions because they provide other benefits. If, on the other hand, the findings of our research turn out to be more troublesome, we will have taken prudent steps towards solving the problem in a cost effective way. I think that such a 'no regrets' policy is particularly justified now in the Eastern European countries, facing a number of urgent social and economic problems, scarce in capital and other resources.

My final answer to the question raised in the beginning of my talk is that if the Western targets are to stabilise the emission of greenhouse gases say in the coming decade, up to the year 2000, then probably the Eastern European countries will reach similar results and this will be done not because the climate issue will be taken as a driving force, but due to a number of other reasons:

(1) The restructuring of economy;

(2) more rational energy use;

(3) new environmental legislation; and

(4) modernised technology.

It should not be expected that the climate warming itself may serve as a driving force for actions aimed specifically at stabilising, for example, the climate. In the coming decade, the Eastern European economies will be simply too weak to spend money for actions which may or may not bring benefits in the middle of the next century.

17

PREVENTATIVE OR CURATIVE ACTION?

Professor Donald H. Pearlman

Partner, Patton Boggs & Blow, former Executive Assistant to
US Secretary of Energy and Secretary of Interior

As evidenced by the earlier portion of these proceedings, there is considerable disagreement amongst knowledgeable scientists about whether increased greenhouse gas emissions from human activities will result in unacceptable climate change. Although the scientific debate is not resolved, policy makers, nevertheless, are confronted even today with vexing questions – should nations now adopt policy measures and, if so, which ones? – that are aimed at preventing environmental threats that are perceived by some, but not by others.

These policy issues are being addressed in both international and national fora. A month ago the International Negotiating Committee for a Climate Change Convention, under the auspices of the General Assembly of the United Nations, began formal work on trying to negotiate an international framework convention on this subject. It is clear that all segments of society have to be concerned with the issue of potential climate change, after all we share a common environment and we have to remember that, by definition, global climate change, if it should occur, would have the potential of environmental, social and economic consequences felt all around our shrinking world.

By the same token, policy measures that are imprudently pursued in an effort to prevent possible climate change could have adverse international, as well as national, economic and social consequences that, among other things, could impede the ability or even the motivation of nations to deal appropriately with the whole array of other environmental problems that confront societies.

I think we can all agree that potential climate change is much more than merely a scientific issue.

It requires integrated policy analysis that draws both from the physical and the social sciences, including specifically economic considerations. In its deliberations on policies pertinent to the climate change issue, the international community has given some, but very, very limited attention to the possibility of curative or adaptation measures. That approach deals with limiting or, at least, ameliorating the adverse consequences of potential climate change, rather than preventing or limiting the causes.

It is impossible, at this time, to evaluate the wisdom of adaptation or curative measures for a lot of reasons. These include our essential lack of information about what we would have to do, the technical feasibility of various adaptation measures and, of course, the economic costs. For those reasons, the ongoing policy debate, particularly in the international community, has been focusing on preventative measures. Some politically very powerful forces are urging adoption of the so-called 'precautionary principle' which originally asserted:

> "Where there are threats of serious or irreversible damage, lack of full scientific certainty should not be used as the reason for postponing measures to prevent environmental degradation."

The precautionary principle gained fame at the Burgin Conference in May 1990. It has been put relentlessly by its very capable advocates, primarily from Western European nations. That approach is seriously flawed because, as used by its advocates, it seriously denigrates the scientific debate. However, even more important the precautionary principle has become an invitation also to ignore, except

Global Warming: The Debate
Edited by Peter Thompson with the assistance of John P. O'Hara
© 1991 Strategy Europe Ltd. Published 1991 by John Wiley & Sons Ltd

for lip episodic service, the economic costs and consequences of the very policies being advocated by those who invoke the precautionary principle. It is almost as though once scientific certainty is ruled out as a barrier to a policy measure, just about anything is justified as long as it alleged to prevent potential climate change.

I think we should be gratified by the little noticed change in the definition of the precautionary principle. It was an affirmation of the importance of economic analysis that was set forth in the Ministerial Declaration of the Second World Climate Conference. As modified by the Ministers at that Conference, the precautionary principle now precludes lack of full scientific certainty as a reason to postpone only cost effective measures. Nevertheless, despite a lack of cost effective or cost benefit analysis of proposals being advocated by them, largely from the European community and some of its members in particular, exceedingly aggressive governmental policies are now being urged, primarily to reduce the emissions of carbon dioxide.

The focus of these advocates is on the industrialised nations. They are good politicians. They know full well that if global climate change were to occur it would be a consequence of human activities occurring all around the world. The advocates of aggressive government policies also know that there is no way, at least for a number of years, to persuade the developing nations to agree now to the same types of limitations that the advocates of those policies would seek to impose upon the industrialised nations.

Estimates are that greenhouse gas emissions from the developing countries will leap from 26% of the world's total in 1985, to about 44% of the world's total by the year 2025. Those nations are smart, they are not about to agree to limiting, much less reducing, their emission to any material degree. Hence the politically astute development of a double standard. Ever since the Nordwig Declaration in 1989, it has become very fashionable for the political declarations of international bodies considering the climate change issue to draw a clear distinction between what is going to be expected of the industrialised nations and what will not be expected of the developing nations. Those differences in stand-ards or policy expectations have not been negotiated but you can count on the fact that the developing nations, which greatly out-number those nations in the industrialised world, are going to resist anything that is even remotely comparable to what some people have in mind for your countries.

Unquestionably, the primary objective of the advocates of aggressive government policy is the imposition on the industrialised nations of what are commonly referred to as targets and timetables for limitation or reduction of greenhouse gas emissions. The most modest of the targets and timetables being proposed is stabilisation of emissions at current levels by the year 2000. Some proposals are more ambitious: they would force industrialised nations to reduce their carbon dioxide emissions from current levels by as much as 20% (the target year varies from the year 2005 to the year 2025).

Those pushing targets and timetables have taken square aim at the carbon dioxide emissions coming from energy use and production. There probably has been some reference to a comprehensive approach on all greenhouse gases, but the unmistakable specific target of governmental action that is now being debated is energy produced carbon dioxide. We have to view these proposals for stabilisation or reduction of carbon dioxide for what they are. They are prescriptions to bring about fundamental changes in the ways that we produce, price and consume energy.

Prime Minister Brundtland referred to a restructuring of our economies, but an adequate supply of energy undergirds the economic viability of both the industrialised nations and the developing nations and, that being true, the stark issue facing policy makers is – what happens to our economies if we go about pursuing some of the policy recommendations of those who are involved in the debate?

We are only now beginning to achieve preliminary economic analysis that will inform policy makers and the public who are served by policy makers, of the potentially gigantic cost to our economies that would result from the imposition of such measures. It is not my purpose to interview those studies in great detail, but rather to try to draw some conclusions from them. Before doing so, it is proper to note that many of these forecasts depend on the ccuracy of the forecasts of energy supply and consumption. That reminds me of a comment of a former Deputy Secretary of the United States who said:

> "Energy forecasters were invented to make economists, by comparison, look respectable."

There have been several macro economic studies which have been collected by an inter-agency task force of my government. On the basis of the preliminary review that they engaged in, it is possible to make the following observations, at least generally:

1) Economic costs will vary from country to country, depending upon a variety of factors. A study indicated that, if developing nations stabilised their carbon dioxide emissions at twice the present levels while the OECD nations cut their emissions 20% from 1990 levels, by the year 2020 there would be average annual losses of projected GDP of about 3% in the United States, to 1% to 2% in most of the OECD countries, to as much as 9% to 11% in China for the period 2040 to 2100.

2) For the United States, where energy is a major input, these studies concluded:

> "They suggest that energy price increases at least as large as those experienced between 1973 and 1985 would be required to achieve widely discussed targets for CO_2 emission reduction. On balance, there is no reason to believe that any attempt to reduce energy use significantly today would be substantially less economically disruptive than were the oil shocks of the 1970s."

If that conclusion is correct, it should greatly alarm those countries which have energy intensity which is roughly the substantial equivalent of that in the United States, such as the United Kingdom.

(3) The projections of world economic costs, to the extent that they exist at all, resulting from policies for global stabilisation, or 20% reduction, range from about 1% to 4% of world growth product per year. That implies staggering consequences, particularly if world population grows as surely we must anticipate that it will. The necessary consequence, of course, is a shocking drop in average per capita income around the world.

These studies of potential economic costs of climate changes are positively frightening, of course, but they are not enough. They have got to be augmented, and this was explicitly recognised by the Inter-governmental Panel on Climate Change which observed, rather wisely I think in its first assessment report:

> "The information available to make sound policy analysis is inadequate because of, among other things, uncertainty with respect to the costs, effects on economic growth and other economic and social implications of specific response options or groups of options."

It makes no sense at all for policy makers to embark upon taxation or regulatory measures designed to avert potential climate change without a far better understanding than we currently have about the economic costs of those policies. Numerous issues have to be addressed, including:

(1) The impacts on economic growth for both industrialised and developing nations.

(2) International trade competition advantages and disadvantages, for example how will the European Community fare in competition with Japan whose economy is much less energy-intensive than most of the countries in the European Community?

(3) Potential flight of capital from industrialised nations to the developing nations that do not impose costly energy reduction or energy related policies.

What is the risk that aluminium or steel or other energy-intensive companies seriously will consider moving their operations or expanding new plant facilities in countries, for example, that do not need to hike dramatically their electricity prices in order to meet and impose obligatory targets and timetables?

(4) Transfer of wealth from north to south and not only by reasons of flight of capital, but also because of the vast funding of new technologies that the developing countries expect to receive from the industrialised nations of the world, or at least from their governments.

(5) The technical, social and administrative feasibility of some of the schemes that have been talked about, such as having worldwide caps and then creating emissions entitlements.

(6) The cost of alternative energies, strategies, the cost of adaptation policies, for example, about which we know so little.

(7) Most importantly, the cumulative economic consequences of the miriad of immediate policy measures, all of which are pursued in the interests of protecting our common environment. Potential climate change is only one of many important issues that our nations face and it must be dealt with, but nobody has yet calculated that total costs of all of these policies, all of which are designed to protect our environment.

When weighing these potentially huge economic costs perceived by some economists against the potentially huge environmental costs perceived by some scientists, and bearing in mind that the perceptions and the conclusions of both groups are debatable, it is more important than ever, to ask the following questions:

(1) Assuming, solely for purposes of argument, that both groups – the scientists and the economists – are more or less right with the benefit to human kind from incurring the economic costs, specifically how much unacceptable global climate change will be averted and for how long if policy measures were to adopt the preventative measures such as targets and timetables for limitations of greenhouse gas emissions?

(2) How much unacceptable climate change would be averted if, notwithstanding the pursuit of these policies by the industrialised nations, the developing nations do not because of the political inability of the international community to impose those types of agreements on the developing nations?

(3) What are the nature and magnitude of the environmental risks if policy makers postpone their decision for a reasonable period of time in order to get better answers or, in some cases, answers at all even on a preliminary basis?

The advocates of preventative actions, such as targets and timetables, cannot give credible answers to those questions. Instead, the IPCC made clear that one of the reasons that the information available to make sound policy analyses is inadequate is:

> "Because of the uncertainty with respect to how effective specific response options, or groups of options, would be in actually averting potential climate change."

In the absence of a reasonable assessment of both the environmental benefits and the economic costs of these proposals, policy makers, I submit, lack the central building block to make rational decisions. Basically, they just do not know how much 'bang for the buck' they are going to get, or 'bang for the pound'.

Mr Hartley talked about insurance. Is it not wise, he suggested, to take out a certain amount of insurance against the risks. The analogy to insurance breaks down. Consider, for example, you or I buy insurance against the risk that our home will be destroyed by fire. We know how much that premium will cost and we also know how much benefit we are going to get. It is fixed by the agreement that we have. With respect to global climate change, we do not know either the economic costs, much less the benefits that we are going to gain from incurring those economic costs, and that is why the analogy to insurance breaks down.

That does not mean that policy makers should refrain from pursuing sensible policies. They are cost effective policies that are justifiable in their own right, they are the so-called 'no regrets' policies. Certainly at, or near, the top of the list would be increased investment in energy technology research and development and we also should pay attention to sensible policies to facilitate the transfer of modern technologies to those developing nations whose greenhouse gas emissions otherwise would grow so rapidly. If that is going to be done, it should be done pursuant to discussions and meaningful dialogue with those developing nations, as well as with the nations whose economies are in transition to market based economies, such as the economies of certain nations in Eastern Europe. When we are transferring technologies, we are transferring those that are specifically suited to the needs of the recipient as determined by the recipient, not by those nations that happen to possess those technologies in the first place.

Of course, there will be costs entailed with those 'no regrets' policies, but at least they appear to have the multiple benefits of providing increased economic opportunities for industrialised nations, improving standards of living for people all around the world and, perhaps, averting a portion at least of the environmental threat, or such environmental threat as may exist.

Preventative action is the question before us this morning. Of course, to the extent that it makes sense, but not when it is merely the product of an uninformed rush to judgement; not when it fails to consider economic considerations, as well as the environmental aspects of the question.

QUESTIONS

(1) QUESTION: Mr Van der Burgt
                Shell International

I have a question for Mr Pearlman. Of course, I do agree with you that we cannot impose on under-developed nations what we have to do which would be criminal, but I would like to question some of your figures.

You were talking about energy consumption in the United States and in Great Britain. The only two countries which are on a par in per capita consumption is the DDR and Czechoslovakia. This is a very clear indication that this use of energy, of the consumption, is definitely not an indicator for the quality of life.

What nations, such as Great Britain, Western Europe and Japan, show is that with a lot less energy

consumption per capita you can still get a good life. Moreover, what we can do in the West is setting an example for the under-developed countries which they can later adopt, so that they will benefit from it at the same time.

I would add further, we should look in the future and I think what we do with CO_2 is driving a car around a curve which we cannot see around. That is very dangerous. It is not necessarily an eighteen wheeler we have to be afraid of, but whatever comes when we see it, it is too late.

ANSWER: Professor Pearlman

Of course quality of life in some nations in Western Europe is every bit as good as it is in the United States or the United Kingdom and yet there is less energy intensity or lower use of energy in terms of gross national product, but let me suggest that there are some differences that explain that. For example, in the United States you have a geographic factor that is entirely unknown to most of the nations of Western Europe. Sheer size forces the movement of raw materials from the western part of the country to the industrialised heartland in the central part or the east. We are talking about an expanse of over three thousand miles where people have to go ahead and have those movements. You then manufacture the commodities in the central or eastern part of the country and re-distribute it throughout the balance of the country. That takes nothing but energy.

Related to that is the fact that our population density is much less in the United States than it is in Western Europe, as a consequence of which you have to move people to their jobs if nothing else. That, of course, is a factor which requires additional consumption of energy. I might point out also that some of the industrialised countries that do have higher energy intensity are also nations that produce energy-intensive products. There are some nations in Western Europe, for example, that do not have substantial production of aluminium which fairly gulps electricity during its manufacture. As a consequence of which, a lot depends on the make up of the economies and it is really not fair to go ahead and compare one against the other by reason of the difference in the make up, as well as the geographical factor that I mentioned earlier.

(2) QUESTION: Mr Evans
Western Mining Corporation,
Australia

I would like to pick up a comment which Mr Hartley made in connection with the great storms of 1987, where he said that we could probably get a better estimate of the damage caused by that storm if we asked people what they are prepared to pay to avoid it.

This refers to what is known as contingent valuation. I thought it would be a good idea if I gave the conference the results of a recent contingent valuation study that has taken place in Australia where people were asked what they would be prepared to pay in order to prevent the mining of what is known as 'Coronation Hill' which is a two or three square mile area not far from Kakagoo National Park. The results came out that the people of Australia were prepared to pay $700 million annually to keep Coronation Hill in its present state and the result was greeted with a great deal of laughter and derision.

I merely make this point to suggest that contingent valuation and conclusions based upon it are fraught with very great danger and I would suggest that any policy proposals based on it should be very seriously considered.

ANSWER: Mr Hartley

I don't disagree with you that they are difficult techniques to use.

(3) QUESTION: I Cook AEA Fusion

This is a question to Mr Hartley in the first instance. In the investment section of your talk, I was surprised to find no mention of the value of the development of new systems of central electricity generation which would make no contribution to the greenhouse effect, and yet would not be subject to the problems of public acceptance that might arise if existing nuclear systems were expanded on

a large scale all over the world. I am referring to fusion or passively safe fission systems.
ANSWER: Mr Hartley

As an economist, I do not have enough knowledge of that. I would like to rely on a technologist to advise on me on that. If there are such options which are well worth the investment, then I am sure they should be pursued, but I do not think I am really the person to answer that.

(4) QUESTION: M Grubb, Energy and
Environmental Programme

A few comments and questions primarily for Donald Pearlman, but perhaps broader on the panel.

First, just quickly on the less developed countries. It seems to me that it is far more complex than you are hinting. In the first place, the vast majority of emissions historically and even currently are from the industrial nations and even in terms of increases since the oil price falls of the mid-1980s, the increases in industrial countries have been larger in absolute terms, but certainly not in relative terms than in developing countries. Developing countries do accept that it is a global problem and are prepared to treat it in a global manner, providing their special circumstances are recognised. I think when talking about emissions per person being a tenth or even a twentieth of industrial countries, one can recognise there are some fairly special conditions involved. I do not think it is as clear cut as you are suggesting.

Secondly, you made the comment that the OPEC price rises were damaging and one would expect the effects of price rises concerning CO_2 abatement to be equally damaging. I think that is a wrong statement. The OPEC price rises were first of all extremely sudden, very large and unplanned, and the resource flows went to other countries. That is why they did have a substantial impact on industrial countries. There is absolutely no parallel, as far as I have been able to see from any of the economic literature, that can easily be drawn between that and phased-in attempts to bring up the price of fossil fuels within industrial countries and collect the revenues and have the choice as to how that is spent.

Thirdly, overall and longer term costs could be very high, but it is a bit like the costs of potential impacts that are quantified measures of global warming. It depends very much on how they are presented. Yes, when we are talking about potentially many billions of pounds, several percent off GNP, but it is a fraction of a percent off GNP growth, and the talk about the impact on lifespans etc – that is not what one is really talking about. The costs of changing or substituting fossil fuels are just not big enough to have that kind of dramatic impact on the economic growth.

My final point related to that, for all the people on the panel, it seems to me that we are being presented with a slightly black and white picture in which there is either adaptation or very high costs. From the starting point, there will be changes and we will have to adapt to them. As far as one can tell even from quite stringent emission scenarios, we still get a doubling effect of CO_2. Is it not, in a way, more helpful to focus on what are the short term measures which we know will not cost a great deal and will have a marginal impact in reducing rates of change etc, of which there actually seem to be quite a lot. I think we are looking very far ahead, and looking at very big numbers which are extremely uncertain, and then getting so frightened that one does nothing. It is not a terribly helpful way to go about the whole problem.

ANSWER: Mr Pearlman

Let me merely make a comment with respect to the willingness of developing nations to get with it in terms of reducing greenhouse gas emissions. I will quote for you precisely the proposal of one of the more nearly involved and vocal developing countries who have very much been involved in the international deliberations so far. This occurred two weeks ago in Chantilly at the first negotiating session of the International Negotiating Committee. That nation proposed that the report of the first negotiating session include the following statement:

"Many countries emphasise that a framework convention and any related legal instruments should impose no limitation on the emissions of developing countries recognising that their energy consumption levels should increase in order for them to satisfy their social and economic development needs."

The fact of the matter is that we are seeing in the international negotiations, at least from the perspective of this one individual, a situation where the developing nations largely are saying:

"Go to it industrialised nations – you go ahead and reduce your emission and, meanwhile, please understand that aside from the fact that you should feel quite guilty about the fact that you have pumped up these greenhouse gas emission in prior years, we the developing countries have the need to grow, and by golly we are going to and we are not going to impede that growth by any material limitation on our own greenhouse gas emissions."

That, from my perspective, is the way the developing nations are looking at it. There is absolutely no indication that the developing nations, taken as a whole, are willing to engage in any significant change in what otherwise would be the course of their greenhouse gas emissions.

ANSWER: Professor Kaczmarek

Eastern European countries cannot be compared neither with Western industrialised countries, nor with the developing countries. They are in a completely different situation. To some extent, we may say that they are over-industrialised in the sense of the role industry in GNP which is much higher in Eastern Europe than in Western Europe, for example. The main problem is the efficiency of economy, the efficiency of the industry. Of course, to improve this efficiency, to modernise our industrial technologies, this will cost some money. As I said before, we have also a number of many pressing environmental problems which have to be solved for the benefit of people.

I am not against any action which may lead to stabilising the CO_2 emissions, for example, if this will at the same time help in solving other problems in our countries, other economic and environmental problems. It is feasible, but there is a need for some investments and a need for reasonable economic policy.

ANSWER: Mr Hartley

Can I just address the points about costs and the point which Michael Grubb made about the analogy about the oil price shock. I think the point is well taken and I agree with what he says about that.

There have been references to the work which various economists have done of the costs of the policies taken to reduce CO_2 emissions. What is clear from this work is that economists do have the tools to enable one to look at the costs over a twenty to thirty year period, up to perhaps thirty years, and it is very clear that if you impose large and fast shocks on the economy that is going to have a very big cost.

Where I think I start to have doubts is to when the economists start to tell me or suggest what is going to happen in terms of cost over a hundred year period. The truth of the matter is, I think, that economists have never really been very good at explaining the long run determinants of economic growth. To suggest in this context that economists can really tell us what the costs are going to be in fifty years ahead, is really putting economics further than at the moment it can go.

(5) QUESTION: Dr Wiesebach, UNIDO

I am with UNIDO, and we are very much concerned with the issue of the working countries versus industrialised countries.

It is, I think, quite correct that a number of developing countries are feeling that this is not for us, this is for the others. I think that position is correctly presented here, but I think this is a very short sighted position, not because of your analysis of possible economic breakdowns and negative effects, but because whatever we do the world is in a technological race and this race is also determined by the environmental concerns. There is a lot about technology being introduced to save energy because it is costly and so on. Of course, developing countries are fooling themselves if they think that by opting out of that race they will be that much better off.

There are not many here from that part of the world, so there is very little point in pursuing this debate but if one does not point to the objective developments which are inherent in that technology race, then we are losing a very important part of the argument.

Part VI

The Business Response
to Global Warming

THE INDUSTRIAL SECTOR'S
VOLUNTARY CODES OF PRACTICE

Dr Horst Wiesebach

Deputy Director of United Nations
Industrial Development Organisation

I have been requested to make an address on the challenging subject of the development and application of the various methods of achieving an implementation of environmental protection measures in industry, such as statutory controls imposed by governments and voluntary codes of practice adopted by industry to safeguard the environment.

This is, indeed, a complex subject and it is timely to start an assessment of statutory controls and voluntary practices as a contribution to the forthcoming United Nations conference on environment and development which will be held in Brazil next year.

I appreciate the opportunity to talk about this topic because UNIDO, is currently debating the same issues in preparing its own strategy for advising client member states on how to achieve sustainable industrial development in a cost effective manner.

In co-operation with the government of Denmark, UNIDO will present results of these deliberations at an international conference on ecologically sustainable industrial development which will be held in Copenhagen in October this year. I will come back to this matter a little later.

There has been considerable debate in the United Kingdom on the merits and demerits of statutory controls and voluntary codes as ways to encourage industries to be responsive to environmental problems. At the end of this debate, you passed the Environmental Protection Act 1990 and, clearly, there was a recognition that voluntary codes of practice, that is broadly formulated statements of good intent by industry groups or trade associations were not always adequate and that statutory controls – that is binding minimum standards – were necessary to meet environmental quality objectives.

In making my remarks, I will not discuss the scientific necessity for, nor the specific reductions needed, to deal with global warming. Instead, I want to share with you my thoughts of policy approaches that are needed to ensure that industrial activities are in line with whatever norms are finally adopted by the political process, or by industry itself.

Perhaps, we could agree that violation of norms for environmental well being and safety have been, and will continue to be, inherent in the process of industrial production. This is a fact of life. The main focus of industrial activity is to transform raw material into goods at the lowest possible cost and in a timely manner. In this process, we know a lot of energy is consumed by certain branches of industry and there is no inherent incentive to mitigate the pollution effects of the production process unless a convincing case can be made that such voluntary activity will lessen the cost of production.

The purpose of environmental policy instruments is to modify this tendency to ignore pollution problems in the production process, and they are intended to modify the behaviour that is naturally characteristic of the free, and I might add also of the planned, economies. We all know that the pollution problem is, if possible, the worst in the completely planned centralised economies.

Global Warming: The Debate
Edited by Peter Thompson with the assistance of John P. O'Hara
© 1991 Strategy Europe Ltd. Published 1991 by John Wiley & Sons Ltd

As we all know, modifying industrial behaviour is difficult and several complementary approaches are needed to accommodate different types of pollutant sources and situations. That is why those who have thought about this subject for many years, such as the OECD, realise that several approaches are necessary to achieve such protection. One can classify these in four ways as:

– Statutory controls

– Voluntary codes

– Economic or market measures and incentives

– Awareness building and training

Statutory controls authorise environmental regulatory programmes and such programmes consist of standards, operating permits for individual facilities, compliance monitoring and sanctions for violaters of standards. Regulatory programmes, having these components, work because they establish specific targets for industrial enterprises and apply meaningful sanctions against those who fail to meet these targets. In plain English, these failures to comply can effect the bottom line of industrial enterprises.

Moral persuasion, on the other hand, appeals to the social responsibility of industrial enterprises and their managers. These appeals take the form of voluntary environmental guidelines such as those, for instance, prepared by the International Chamber of Commerce or, to take another international example, the European Council of Chemical Manufacturers Federations, CEFIC in Brussels or the US Chemical Manufacturers Association (CMA). There are also other national federations of industry like the CBI in the United Kingdom or the BDE in Germany that have been issuing many such codes so there exists already a spate of these documents.

They usually cover general aspects of waste management and sometimes commitment to use clean technology. In the case of the CEFIC, they will also, in the next month I believe, cover the whole issue of transfer of technology where the chemical industry after the Bopal accident had special reason to see to it that the technologies are handled in a proper manner. The only sanction available against those not complying with the voluntary codes is to expel them from the group or association, a move which probably has little real effect as membership in a trade association is not necessarily a prerequisite for carrying on a business, although it could become a strong motive being a member. In other words, failure to comply with the codes of conduct does not effect the bottom line of the industrial enterprises, work.

Economic incentives are governmental interventions that change market structures for the express purpose of environmental improvement. Such examples now slowly come up. They can be micro-economic incentives such as fees and marketable permits. Other examples of a more macro-economic nature are changes in the tax structures, import policies and subsidies.

Economic instruments, which are also often called market based incentives, differ from those statutory controls as they do not impose fixed emission limits as the statutory controls, rather they rely on voluntary decisions by enterprises. Clearly, economic incentives can effect the bottom line of industrial enterprise, but they are often preferred to regulatory programmes because they offer a range of choices and encourage the search for solutions, less costly than those imposed by the public authorities.

Finally, awareness raising and training are outreach efforts by governments and associations to inform and assist enterprises to meet environmental objectives, at least cost. In some case, these efforts have shown enterprises how they can reduce the total cost of production by meeting environmental requirements. One only has to look at the success stories from companies in Europe and in the United States, certainly these efforts provide an economic inducement to enterprises to comply, that they can reduce the cost of meeting economic targets and, in some cases, are actually good investments.

Clearly, the technical solutions that emerge from such an out-reach programme can effect the bottom line because they can result in a comparative cost advantage for those firms adopting these solutions. We feel that these instruments could, on an international basis, also very much be used to mitigate the problems between the north and the south by using technical assistance as a type of out-reach to assist in the application of such methods.

What one can deduce from this characterisation of alternative policy approaches is the following:

The relative merits of statutory controls and voluntary codes are that we have here not exclusive applications, but rather supplementary activities of the government and of industry. We should think that all four of the listed measures could be used at the same time in order to minimise, if not eliminate even, pollutant discharges. As one would not expect that the voluntary codes, as such, would work in a sufficient manner, as the evidence suggests, we would wish to see the other three applied alongside with them. As you know, voluntary codes do not carry sanctions and, therefore, do not give a sufficient motive to follow the best technology or the least emission standards.

We all know that very often such activities to minimise pollution are very costly but, on the other hand, we have seen in recent years that industry's perspective about covering the cost of such regulation has been changing to some extent because they have found out that the cost of mitigation very often was not nearly as significant as industry had anticipated, for instance, when the debate began in the early 1970's.

In fact, some industries and some firms are now realising that pollution prevention pays. The emergence of green industrialists such as, for instance, the group of Baum which is the German Environmental Management Association (which now has a affiliate here in England called Tree, and another one in France called Arbre) and also the commitments of some of the major chemical companies in the US, to reduce toxic pollutants beyond the regulatory requirements, show that enterprises are starting to realise that there is some merit in environmental regulation and they even go beyond this. This, by the way, is one of the principles of the Baum Group. If they see governmental regulation and we can go beyond it, we should do so.

Let me turn back to the voluntary codes proper because they have a lot of merit. They are useful for several purposes:

– These codes serve to sensitise managers of industrial enterprises to emerging environmental issues and to encourage them to incorporate an appropriate response in their corporate planning. As you well know, anticipative and preventive actions are often less costly then responsive and curative ones.

– Codes can show environmental regulators that enterprises are aware of environmental concerns, so commitments to codes can help restore trust on the part of regulators in industry to act in a responsive and responsible manner. In the long run, this trust can result in regulatory strategies which give enterprises more degrees of freedom in responding to environmental objectives.

– Codes can help in countries where there are inadequate statutory requirements, such as in the third world countries. They can provide enterprises with a responsible and defensible basis for environmental actions.

– Codes can assist in making small and medium sized enterprises aware of environmental goals. Government regulatory programmes cannot reach these thousands of small enterprises.

Although I am somewhat sceptical about this last point, I do see some potential in reaching small and medium sized enterprises indirectly through another method, namely through the large enterprises who adopt the codes. If these large enterprises deal only with environmentally responsible contractors and suppliers as is, for instance, recommended by the founder of the Baum Group, by George Winter in his book 'Business and the Environment', then there is a significant potential for effecting the actions of those suppliers, that is the small and medium scale industry. Indirectly they are forced into a more positive environmental stance.

How might these various policy approaches be relevant for mitigating the emissions of greenhouse gases?

We need to chose policy approaches that are both effective and cost minimising because of the potentially large cost of stabilising the global temperature. Although there is no consensus on an emission reduction target, the cost of meeting some of the targets will be high, for example in the United States expenditures on environment controls now constitute about 2% of the gross national product and expenditures for reducing greenhouse gases in the United States are estimated to range between 2% and 8% of the gross national product. The lower estimate would even double the current expenditure level and, of course, the upper estimate would result in environmental expenditures equal in size to the expenditures for medical services in the United States.

In the light of the seriousness and the cost of these challenges, I believe we should make use of all the four policy approaches outlined above.

Statutory Controls
Here, we would need to develop a protocol just as we did for the CFC's to reduce the release of greenhouse gases. You already heard about the work going on in the context of the United Nations as a result of the IPCC's studies, so I will not comment on this approach further.

Voluntary Codes
Here, one potential candidate is a code for trade associations that represent multi-national corporations. This code would move beyond an endorsement of the importance of sustainable development to, say, specific concerns for global warming and this would show commitment to the most energy efficient technologies. There is a chance now that the Business Council for Sustainable Development, which was recently created might move in that direction because it groups together some forty or fifty chief executive officers of the largest corporations in the world.

Economic Incentives
Here, as was evident in a recent article in the 'Economist', there is already considerable discus-sion about the use of taxes on production and consumption. Another possibility is a tax rebate for those countries maintaining or creating the capacity to sequester a carbon. Again, in Switzerland, there is a very intensive debate going on with various models put forward on how the taxation system could be used to minimise the use of energy both in energy and domestic consumption.

Awareness and Training
This approach deserves, I think, most attention. In no country has the potential for energy conservation been fully exploited to date. Recent studies have found achievable near term energy conservation potentials of up to 25% in Germany, 30% in the United States, up to 45% in the Netherlands and in Japan. An increasing awareness of this potential and ensuring accomplishments for training will have significant financial and environmental benefits.

The Dow Chemical company, for instance, started an incentive programme and, although it limited the programme to a certain type of investment to reduce energy consumption over eight years, there has been a flow of proposals and the average return on investment of these proposals was 200%. In other words, investment in this area paid for itself within half a year and I would like to see anywhere an investment in the energy generation field that would yield such returns. I do not think it exists any more today. This shows that there is a lot of economic potential and awareness, and building and training makes sense.

The organisation that I represent, UNIDO, is committed to awareness, raising and training in developing countries as the most practical cost effective response to the global concerns. We have ongoing projects that are asisting working countries to recycle and reuse the CFC's and conserve energy. We reach out to all developing countries with our industrial and technical information bank which gives them access to the latest technical information in affordable terms.

In concluding my presentation, I would like to come back to the Ministerial Conference on Ecologically Sustainable Industrial Development. All UNIDO member states are being invited to participate but we would also like to stress that this conference is also open to industry in the sense either to international federations as directly invited organisations, or to national federations as being part of the national delegations. We feel that the involvement of industry is essential to make this a success. It shows you that the United Nations does not need to create a new organisation in order to address the problems of the environment and its protection.

I think it is advantageous to involve as many of these existing organisations as possible and not concentrate on the creation of a new body which would probably be very difficult to put together and will expend our energies on a side activity, instead of the main point, namely protecting the environment in a sustainable way.

19

HOW HAVE BUSINESSES RESPONDED TO ENVIRONMENTAL LEGISLATION?

David Jones

Partner, Masons Solicitors

I am only going to make four points today. I am going to talk about the environment and the commercial reality, then we are going to do a little bit of a legal crash course because I want to take you into the UK legal framework. I am then going to move on to a subject called public perception and enforcement, and then we are going to do a little bit of crystal ball gazing and talk about codified laws, Europe and beyond.

A few months ago, there was an article in the Guardian which was a long interview with Sir Denys Henderson, Chairman of ICI, and he said in relation to the environment and the commercial reality:

> "We are not here simply to clean up the environment. We are here to conduct our operations for the benefit of our shareholders and, hopefully, for our employees in a way which is compatible with what is expected by the public. If, when you have spent money on the environment, the business you have spent it on cannot produce a decent return, then the inevitable conclusion is that you withdraw from those businesses."

I think that what that comment highlights is this dilemma between, on the one hand, the environmentalists who take the understandable view that we are abusing our plant, we only have one place to live, we have got stop and, on the other hand, (particularly with the polluter pays principle that we see in relation to the environment,) business saying that there is a commercial limit to what I can absorb. If you push me too far, then I am simply going to go out of business and my work force is going to end up on the dole queue.

Between those two areas lies, in effect, the law and what I am going to try and do is show how the pendulum of the law moves from time to time, and why it moves. We will start with the very fast crash course on the UK legal framework.

In this country, we have what is called a common law system. This is a system of judicial law making by judges. It is a common law system that has been with us since time began. We have had it for many hundreds of years and one of it cornerstones is the philosophy that one must exercise reasonable skill and care. The difference between this type of law and the codified laws that we see, particularly in Europe, and you also see it in the Middle East, is that they have codified laws very much based upon absolute obligations, the concept of strict liability.

Simply to explain the difference between the two and their effect is, if I say to you that I am going to build you a paper mill that will produce so much paper a week, if I fail to build a paper mill that produces that amount of paper a week, it is an absolute obligation I have breached and, for whatever reason, a liability will arise. If, however, I say as I do in my common law system that I am going to exercise reasonable skill care in constructing this paper mill that will produce so much paper a week and, nevertheless, the paper mill fails to produce that amount of paper per week, if I have still exercised reasonable skill and care then no liability will arise.

That is the very significant difference between these two types of laws and the interesting thing that the UK faces is that, through the European Directives, we are seeing a great number of codified laws very much based upon absolute obligations. For many people, this concept will be quite difficult to take on board.

If I can go back, I think that one of these sort of misnomers about environmental law, is a lot of people think in our system, because we have had some Acts recently like the 1989 Water Act and the recent Environmental Protection Act, environmental law has been with us for about three years. That is not right because it has again been with us for hundreds of years. We can go back in common law to the law as to noise, nuisance and trespass and, indeed, in 1868 there was a case that dealt with dangerous substances being taken on to land. A lot of those environmental issues have long been with us, but all that law of course is based upon then, in this country, the agricultural base of England. We were than an agricultural economy.

What has happened in the Twentieth Century is that we have moved to become an industrial based country and, in those circumstances, what one has seen in our common law is intervention by Parliament that has started passed statutes that reflect this industrial change. When you get to the Twentieth Century, parliament starts to pass statutes relating to the environment. In 1906, we have the Coal Works Regulation Act. We go into the 1930s where we have the two Public Health Acts. We go into the 1950s where we have the Clean Air Acts. We go into the 1960s with some River Pollution Acts. We go into the 1970s with the Health and Safety at Work. We then, of course, get into the 1980s with the Water Act and 1990 with the Environmental Protection Act.

What these statutes have done is they have responded to demands as this country has changed, that we should have legislation. One tends to find in terms of looking at how business responds, the answer is that there is a public awareness for change. Parliament comes in with draft legislation and then thereafter business does respond because it has new regulations to comply with. One has to say, up until most recently, that the environmental legislation in this country to the Twentieth Century, has tended to come rather slowly. It is now, however, really beginning to gather pace, particularly when you get to Europe.

The way that Parliament does intervene, perhaps the best most recent example and particularly as we have had quite a lot of discussion on voluntary codes, is how Parliament decided that the voluntary code procedure, in relation to North Sea oil rigs, had to come to an end following Piper Alpha and, therefore, the self-regulatory procedures that the oil industry adopted is now to be changed and Parliament has now decided, as with the construction industry, that it is going to move in the Health and Safety Executive. There's now legislation to change the way in which health and safety is going to be approached in the oil industry.

The important thing about statutes is that what statutes create, if you breach those statutes, are fines. They are criminal fines and the criminal law tends to come up front ahead of the civil law, as I talked about earlier when I went back hundreds of years on the common law. The effect of criminal fines, and environmental legislation creates criminal fines if you breach the regulations, is from a business point of view quite worrying because the first thing is that, if you are fined, there is no way that you can transfer the risk of that fine, if you so elect, into say an insurance policy. If the fine comes, it is straight off the top of the company accounts and it is going to hurt you.

The other thing one has to bear in mind is that a lot of these regulations, when they come, are creating these absolute obligations and so the defences to breaching these regulations are potentially and increasingly very unforgiving. For a lot of business, they may become really quite frightened as they see themselves being fined and, of course, under the Environmental Protection Act the cap has really come off it because we are now into unlimited fines and we have started to see the effects of that with Shell and the million pound fine for polluting the Mersey.

Having said all that, we have one point to make and that is you can have as many laws as you like. You can have hundreds of laws, but as to whether those laws are any good really depends on two things:

(1) Public perception

(2) Enforcement

Dealing with public perception, we have a law in this country called the Sunday Trading Laws. This means that people are not meant to go shopping on a Sunday. Shops are not meant to open. That is the religious day when we should all be going to church. Of course, we saw just before Christmas, that law is simply being abused. People went to a shop on a Sunday, the shops were keen to open on a Sunday because business is down and, therefore, the public perceive that particular law as a law they intend to ignore and, indeed, in their thousands they ignore it, the result of which is the local authorities, who are left with the obligation to enforce that law, have rather given up. I suppose at some stage parliament will eventually decide that there has to be a change to this law because the public disregard it.

The poll tax really is now a tax that is in disarray. I think it was reported earlier this week that there are no fewer than fourteen million people who are not paying it and I think that, it is fair to say the law, as relating to the collection of poll tax, is now suffering from both political and legal chaos.

Having said all that, I think the thing about global warming is that, from the public's perception, this tends to be a rather distant subject. After all, if you look at the debate you have now, you are looking to the year 2000, the year 2005. For many members of the public, that is just too far away and it may be that the legislation side of global warming will take some time to catch up. That would not, for instance, apply to say contaminated land. That, in this country, is becoming very topical. Therefore, we have seen in the last two or three years a tremendous increase in the amount of regulatory law dealing with contaminated land.

The second aspect which I touch upon is enforcement. The point about these statutory laws in this country, unlike in America, is that we do not have class actions. You cannot create a body that goes pursuing a particular company for breaching these regulations. This function is left to public authorities set up by parliament, or alternatively the crown. They are the people who prosecute and they prosecute companies for breaching these regulations.

In relation to water, the 1989 Water Act set up the National Rivers Authority to monitor the pol-lution of rivers and, in fact, to take steps to stop this pollution. I think there are now arising in this country, two schools of thought to the NRA. First of all, it is a good thing to have the NRA. It has made a good start, after all look at Shell, and we hope it is going to continue. There are the cynics coming in and saying 'this is all very well, but rumour has it that next year's budget, courtesy of the Treasury, could see a cut in the amount of money that is going to be given to the NRA'. In which case the NRA could find itself in difficulties as to enforcement.

If you do not give people the power to enforce then, frankly, all that will happen to the law is that it will exist on the statute book and will be taken no further.

I now come to my bit of crystal ball gazing and that really is European Directives. To date, Brussels have passed about two hundred and eighty Directives dealing with the environment. It is all codified law. It is drafted by people who are used to codified law and it creates strict liability. The duty of care, the reasonable skill and care has gone. It is the absolute obligation. One thing about Europe is that they really do enjoy producing Directives and there are many more on the way.

I think, from businesses' point of view, they face the prospect of seeing a lot of these codes produced which create absolute obligations, which create unlimited fines of which they cannot transfer the risk, to which they find they may have no defence. They will come thick and fast and there is nothing they can do to stop it. If that was not bad enough, recently there was a draft Service Directive. It is only in draft and the construction industry has got rather excited about this because they suddenly find themselves to being deemed to be a service industry.

This Directive goes even further when it takes on board the concept of a party being guilty until proven innocent. Our concept, in terms of UK law, is that you are innocent until you are proven guilty. It may well be that we could see on the environment the philosophy adopted by Brussels that you will be guilty until you are proved innocent in relation to these regulations. That, for business, could be horrendous because we will then witness the most serious change to the English legal system ever. Not just in our lifetime, but ever.

In those circumstances, to go back where we started with Sir Denys Henderson, there is a real problem for UK business that with all this coming, they could be simply swept away. They have already to face with codified laws a tide of environmental legislation to come. It is on its way, we know it is coming, and it has got to be dealt with. They ought to have the opportunity, if they can cope with it, to prosper and to develop and to make the appropriate changes. It is not easy because many of those changes involve spending capital sums and we are in a recession.

If they are not careful and they do not start taking decisions that reflect these changes and start to take on board these philosophies, then there is a very serious risk, in my view, that in the next ten years much of the UK business as we know it today will last be seen drowning in the cruel sea of bankruptcy.

20

THE EFFECT OF GLOBAL WARMING ON BUSINESS

David R. Cope

Executive Director of UK CEED
Chairman of Economies Working Group, Cabinet Office

I have not had the chance to listen to the debate that has gone on so far. However, I think I can make some reasonable assumptions about what would have been discussed and, indeed, I have to because it is based upon what I assume has been discussed that I want to elaborate a thesis or a perspective this afternoon. I assume there has been a great deal of discussion about the conclusions of the Inter-governmental Panel on Climate Change. I think perhaps there will have been discussion about how that has been brought closer to home, in some respects by the work of the Department of the Environment Group, the Climatic Change Impacts Review Group, and I assume that must be the case because I notice that at least one member of that Review Group is here today.

I assume by now that everybody is fairly familiar with the current status of scientific evidence on global warming. I assume that they are fairly familiar with some of the secondary impacts which would be a possible consequence of increases in global mean temperatures, such as the regional variations, and consequent secondary impacts such as potential sea level changes. I have to take all that as given. In particular, I take it as given that there has been a great deal of discussion, up until now, on the levels of uncertainty which are associated with the current level of scientific knowledge.

If that assumption is correct, I want to put one thesis to you, which perhaps has never been elaborated in quite this way although I think it is implicit in the current state of understanding of the phenomenon of global warming: as the uncertainty increases our predictive ability decreases. As one

moves away from long term secular trends, about which we have some information in particular, for example, the actual levels of atmospheric concentrations of carbon dioxide and other radiative forcing gases, to the secondary consequences, we move towards phenomena which are more ephemeral and/or stochastic in their nature, ie based upon the chance coincidence of a number of factors such that we find it more and more difficult to predict them. For example, if you look in the literature at the question of what about, not climatic change, but variability and weather patterns, weather being the short term consequence of a large number of climatic and other long term causal factors, we find that we are less and less able to predict with any degree of certainty.

If that thesis is accepted, I would then attach a consequent argument to that, and that is as one moves from those levels where we have a reasonable degree of certainty to those where we have more and more uncertainty we are moving from those issues which are comparatively irrelevant to business, to those which do have some significance for business. As we move up that hierarchy of uncertainty, we are moving closer and closer to the issues which are concerned with business.

I should say that my interpretation of business as being both the manufacturing industry and commerce and also, most importantly, agriculture and associated extractive and/or regenerable activities. In other words, I am taking business as meaning all the activities of wealth creation in which we engage as human beings.

Global Warming: The Debate
Edited by Peter Thompson with the assistance of John P. O'Hara
© 1991 Strategy Europe Ltd. Published 1991 by John Wiley & Sons Ltd

For many individuals, the issues of global warming seem somewhat far away and are perhaps potentially, therefore, less relevant than many other issues which impinge upon daily life. Some weeks ago, I sat down and began to think about this issue as it appertains to decision making within business. It seems to me that business, perhaps as an extension of our own individual interests, would prefer a world which was homeostatic, where there was no change at all, or at least perhaps where there would be only one change, from which all other changes might flow and that would be a change upwards in the level of profit accruing to industry.

There are, of course, the challenges of change for its own sake, which I am sure attract those who participate in business just as they attract those who participate in any other activity. Generally speaking, I think it would be fair to argue that business would prefer if nothing else changed around it. Indeed, a lot of business decision are attempts to try and control the rate of change in those other parameters in order that decisions can be taken which are focused in on achieving a desired rate of change.

I thought to myself, what are the changes which are going on around business decision taking which impinge upon that process, and how do these compare in the nature of their change to the changes which we can make reasonable assumptions about in connection with global warming? I am not going to elaborate on those assumptions about global warming, as I said, because I assume that you have talked about those already.

I looked at these sort of circumstances in which industry finds itself and I tried to single out what I thought were some measures of the nature of change which has an impact on the business environment. For example, on form of change which we find is where there is a long term secular increase and can we forecast that it will continue to go in that direction? – that is another matter. Written around that are quite phenomenal short term fluctuations and I have picked, for obvious reasons, on the construction industry sector. That industry has experienced phenomenal fluctuations over the past five or six years and I do not need to tell an audience like this about the nature of that change.

Other changes which surround the business sec-tor, in the past at least, have given us more grounds for confidence, at least in terms of extrapolation, that we could forecast, to as reasonable degree, how things might develop in the future.

What about other trends with which business has to deal, such as trends in bank interest rate. Over only the past three years the fluctuations which have occurred are such that the implications of very short term changes have dominated many business decisions over that period.

Business, based upon those sort of trends, has to make reasonable assumptions about how things might develop in the future, but most of those assumptions are based upon gross degrees of uncertainty, or upon articles of faith, the continuation of the entire context of business activity. Do not let me forget to remind you of the way in which one can get phenomenal changes in that such as have occurred in Eastern Europe.

What about those areas where we can forecast into the future with a reasonable degree of certainty? I took as a measure of this, what we can say has a reasonable degree of certainty about demographic changes. I chose to look at the rate of new entrants to business. Again, this is a subject which is well know to business, the down turn in the number of young people able to enter the labour force and management.

We can, with a reasonable degree of accuracy, forecast that trend, assuming that there are not gross demographic catastrophes, for some period of time over which some of the forecasts about the impacts of global warming have been made. There are very few other areas where we can forecast with any degree of certainty.

I am led to conclude that our current state of knowledge is such that for the different sectors of industry, there is a great deal of uncertainty, but what we know with any degree of certainty about the future is such that global warming, as the direct physical and associated impact, will have very little significance for industry over the period of time which it is reasonable to make assumptions about possible trends, compared with other considerations.

Let me qualify immediately what I have just said. I am talking about the direct impact, which I am assuming you have heard about, over the past few days that may occur with the level of current uncertainty about those forecasts. I am not talking about the requirements that might be placed upon industry in terms of dealing with controls of emissions. I am not talking about the consequences of other policies which may be adopted which will have implications for business. I am talking purely about the geophysical changes that we can know about, or make reasonable hypothesis about, for the foreseeable future and what they will mean for the operating context of business. My thesis is that those will be insignificant compared with many of the other fluctuations that business has to deal with in its daily, weekly, monthly yearly decision making processes.

There are some possible exceptions to this. It is not secret that they must be those sectors of business which take very long term decisions. Clearly, in particular, agriculture and perhaps especially forestry may now need to start taking some decisions, in terms of influences and current investment activities, based upon what we now know about the direct physical impacts and associated secondary consequences of global warming.

I would suggest that when we get down to the level of decision taking in other sectors, that generally speaking the fluctuations, the uncertainties, the context that we are talking about associated with global warming are such that it is lost in the noise of uncertainty surrounding the decision making in those sectors, attributed to many of those other variables some of which I have given you some examples of historic change.

One exception to this structure here, and again I am sure there has already been some discussion about it, is that the argument that the insurance industry in particular does need to look very carefully at the whole question of ephemeral extreme events and the extent to which there may be trigger thresholds in some of the climatic changes and associated variables which might precipitate higher levels of extreme occurrences. The Climate Change Impact Review Group at-

tempted, to the best of anybody's current ability, to try and put some figures on that and they produced some interesting data on things like the frequency of extreme hot summers, as we had in 1976, and to a lesser extent last year. That is a partial exception to my overall thesis.

This is, I would hasten to add, not a statement of complacency because, as I have said, I have not in my discussion considered the pressures that will come upon business in order to respond in terms of control of emissions and other considerations, secondary ways of controlling emissions such as organising the distribution of activities and so on and so forth. I have restricted my discussion purely to the extent to which physical and associated land use, changes and so on would impinge upon decision making.

I conclude then by saying that if we want to look at the impact of environment and environmental changes on business, there are far more intense local constraints which will impinge upon business decision taking in any country which are far more significant, in my opinion, than the direct consequences of climatic change. I am talking about things here like land use issues associated with the sheer scarcity of certain types of preferred landscapes throughout most countries of the world. I am talking about the problems which industry will face, along with citizens in terms of their domestic consumption patterns over things like waste management, the constraints and availability of disposal sites for waste. I am talking about some of the constraints that may emerge from the impacts of water pollution in terms of residual build up of pollutants in sources so that they are contaminated for particular purposes, not only drinking water, but various industrial processes which we are seeing already.

I am saying that, compared with these locally determined issues, the direct constraints business will face from the direct consequences, are going to be somewhat insignificant.

21

INDUSTRY ACTION ON
GLOBAL WARMING ISSUES

Christopher Hampson

Director, ICI, Chairman of CBI Environment Committee

Previous speakers, in this session, have talked about how business has been, or will be, affected by global warming and the actions that might flow from worldwide concern on this issue. What I would like to discuss briefly is the positive action which industry is taking in this field and the role that industry might play in future developments. Obviously, in such a short time frame, I cannot do much more than just touch on the main points and, inevitably, draw particularly on the experience of my own company and of the chemical industry with which I am most familiar.

The first point I would like to make is that industry generally is very much alive to the problem of global warming and is taking the issue seriously. In this country, the CBI, as represented by the CBI Environment Committee, has recognised global warming as one of the key areas to which it should devote attention. Two recent papers from the CBI on transport policy and on energy policy have reflected that.

In addition, the CBI has taken a particular interest in promoting energy efficiency among its members and a special Energy Efficiency Working Party as the source of advice and initiatives. Before discussing industry actions, it is probably a good idea to remind ourselves of the contribution by various greenhouse gases and then what might be done about them.

For simplicity today, I would like to concentrate on CO_2 and CFC's, as industry does not have a major direct role in reducing methane, and nitrous oxide except for one or two specific examples, again industry does not have a major role to play.

A survey of CO_2 emissions in the UK in 1987, showed that industry represented approximately one third, directly or indirectly, indirectly mainly as the consumer of electricity. Here, industry has been doing a comparatively good job, at least as compared to other sources of CO_2. Emissions of CO_2 from industrial activity have, in fact, fallen by 50% since 1960. Transportation is the growing consideration, while domestic use has remained fairly steady.

This performance by industry reflects the fact that energy costs have a direct bearing on bottom line profitability. In the UK, for example, manufacturing industry now uses 25% less energy than it did in 1970. The proportion of energy in the UK, used by industry, dropped from 42% in 1960 to 28% of the total in 1989. The part that is actually growing is the transportation sector.

I believe this very good energy efficiency performance in industry reflects mainly the efforts of the energy intensive industries, as this is where the economic incentives are the greatest. For industry generally, energy costs are not always a very large part of their total cost structure, making the economic justification of energy conservation investments difficult, but that is not true, for example, of the chemical industry.

The UK chemical industry is very energy intensive, using about a third of the total energy used by industry, while representing only 10% of total UK manufacturing output. Energy efficiency is, therefore, particularly important. From 1980 to 1987, UK chemicals output grew by 32% or roughly a third, while energy purchases actually reduced by 15%. This represents a 36% decrease of energy use per

Global Warming: The Debate
Edited by Peter Thompson with the assistance of John P. O'Hara
© 1991 Strategy Europe Ltd. Published 1991 by John Wiley & Sons Ltd

unit of output and it has been achieved by new technology and new process equipment, as well as better energy management and more efficiently planned operations.

Specifically in ICI, worldwide since 1971, that is in the last twenty years, production has more than doubled, while energy use has actually been reduced by 10% and CO_2 emissions by 20%. This means that we have more than halved energy use per unit output, while reducing CO_2 per unit of output by two thirds.

Although this may seem impressive, we believe there is still much to be done. In fact, one of the key environmental objectives established by the Chairman of ICI, as announced last year, was to implement an even more rigorous energy and resource conservation programme, from which we expect to have achieved substantial further benefits by 1995. How in fact are we going about doing this?

First of all, a great deal can be accomplished by attention to detail and the use of well known procedures and equipment, by proper maintenance of steam traps, proper insulation of pipes and equipment, attention to effective operation of energy production and energy using equipment, and by computerised energy management – many of the programmes that were referred to I think by some of the previous speakers.

In general, our technical and engineering people believe that these sorts of measures, conscientiously applied, can result in energy savings of at least 5% to 10% in most circumstances. Specific steps to recover waste heat may require investment, but can produce quite significant energy savings and acceptable rewards. I cannot say that we have experienced many of those 200% return projects referred to by previous speakers, but there are still profitable projects that can be undertaken. Of course, the choice of fuels, and particularly reduced reliance on coal, has had an effect on CO_2 emissions.

There are, in fact, many ways to improve the energy efficiency and fuel conservation of existing boiler steam plants. Modern conventional power stations convert only about 36% of the fuel into electricity, with most of the rest wasted as low grade heat. If both heat and power are used, the efficiency is much improved and combined heat and power plants are particularly suitable for industrial applications, as energy efficiency can be doubled in comparison with conventional power stations. In fact, in combined heat and power stations energy efficiencies in the range of 85% are possible. I regret to say that there are relatively few of such plants found here in the UK, although their number is now growing.

One example is the large 1800 megawatt combined heat and power electricity generating plant being built by Teeside Power on the site of our Wilton UK complex. The station will use natural gas obtained through a new direct pipeline from the north sea, with the waste heat providing virtually the total process heat and steam requirement of our petrochemical complex. It will, in addition, supply all local electricity requirements and export the remaining 80% of the electricity to the national grid.

The beneficial environmental impact of this plant is very substantial. When fully operational, and thereby replacing the coal now used to produce this amount of electricity and steam, it will reduce CO_2 emissions for that tranche of electricity by about 50%. In addition, emissions of SO_2 and nitrous oxide will be reduced by 99% and 90% respectively. ICI will obtain about one third of its UK electricity requirements from this plant and we are looking at ways of extending the concept in other locations. Not only does it make significant environmental improvement, it also has a very impressive pay back in reducing the cost of electricity.

In addition to more efficient generation of energy, industry has responded by developing improved technology which is more energy efficient. I would like to give you just one example from processes with which ICI is involved; the production of ammonia, a basic chemical used in many products from fertilisers to plastics. Through a series of process design and technology changes, the energy consumption per tonne of ammonia produced has been reduced by more than two thirds from the old coke based process to today's modern plants. The latest process design, for which we won an environmental award (the LCA process), has brought about reductions compared to the best, at that time, of 87% of NO_X, 95% SO_2, 60% CO_2 and 75% ammonia in liquid effluents. If all ammonia worldwide was produced in this way, then in terms of nitrous oxide emission that would be equivalent to taking over 5 million cars off the road.

Industry will, undoubtedly, also have a role to play in the development of alternative energy source, but here I believe governments must give a clear lead on what they, and by that I mean the community, really wants. Timescales to make a significant import is long and industry can only marshall its resources effectively when it is clear what is required.

The other area where industry can make a significant contribution is in CFCs and CFC replacements. The World Meteorological Organisation estimates the contribution of CFCs to global warming at 15%. However, under the Montreal protocol, and its subsequent revisions, production of CFCs will be phased out, to a large extent, before the end of this century, certainly in the European Community by 1997 and probably before that.

Their impact as greenhouse gases will, despite this, take some time to disappear because of their lifetime which is fifty to hundred and fifty years, and because of the CFCs already in use. On this latter point, a lot of effort has gone into recovering and recycling CFCs, but so far with only limited success. For example, we have set up a recycling service and have worked with a number of Regional Councils who have taken steps to set up recovery schemes. Recovery from large industrial users is happening, but recovery, for example, from scrap refrigerators is difficult and expensive and has not been very successful despite considerable effort.

What about CFC replacement? The products that will replace CFCs in most refrigeration and air conditioning applications are HFCs – hydrofluoro carbons that contain no chlorine and, therefore, have no ozone depleting effect. HFCs, of which the first commercial product is Klea 134a from ICI, do still have a greenhouse gas effect. This is only about a tenth of the greenhouse effect of the CFCs they replace, but is still considerably more than CO_2, a point that is stressed for example by Greenpeace.

However, even if the substitutes were used to the same extent as CFCs, the total contribution to global warming would be one tenth of the current contribution, that is just over 1%. In fact, it is estimated that the HFC market will only amount to about 40% of the market for CFCs, so that the greenhouse or global warming effect of HFCs will be less than 1%.

It is clear that the contribution to warming from CFCs will start to decrease before the end of this century and that the contribution from replacements will be very small and will remain so. Like the CFCs they will replace, these compounds will be used to provide energy efficient refrigeration and insulation.

This latter point is particularly important when considering alternative refrigerant materials. If these do not match the energy efficiency of current systems, they could, in fact, lead to a net increase in global warming due to the CO_2 rise from energy generation. In this respect, HFCs are highly efficient. In current domestic refrigerators, and if you take a twenty year life of a refrigerator, some 7% of the potential global warming, over its lifetime, arises from the CFC refrigerant fluid, 8% from the CFC in the insulation, and the remaining 85% from the carbon dioxide by-product of energy to run a refrigerator.

Substitution by HFCs reduces the potential global warming from the fluid and insulation to less than 2%, while the energy required stays the same. Non-fluorocarbon replacements would have to match the energy efficiency of current systems to avoid a net increase in global warming and the indications are that they fall far short of this goal.

In terms of the future, it is clear that further efforts need to be addressed to industry's possible further contribution to reductions of CO_2 emissions. Here, the fastest growing contribution to CO_2 is in the transportation and domestic market. Thus, while continuing to reduce its own energy usage, I believe industry and government must increasingly turn their attention to the steps that could be taken on these fronts.

Transportation, and particularly the use of automobiles, is a case in point. Various solutions to this problem have been suggested from legislative restrictions on automobile use and increased public transport, reduction of engine size, greater engine efficiency, better mileage automobiles.

However, as I hope I have already demonstrated, industry is an effective means of delivering desirable change if properly motivated. It would seem to me that governments, by the proper choice of economic instruments and certain legislative changes, could encourage industry to develop cars with less impact on the environment. This would be a better route than seeking, by regulations, to try and force the population against their demonstrated will to give up the freedom applied in access to private transportation.

The same could be true of improved energy efficiency and home appliances, or in improved building regulations. Governments should be seeking to harness market forces and industry to work towards desirable goals. The area of government intervention and the use of economic instruments to encourage industry and the public along the right paths, requires more debate and more thought and research.

An example often raised is the desirability of a carbon tax or a carbon reduction tax. Higher prices, undoubtedly, encourage energy conservation and vice versa. The oil shock at the beginning of the 1980s brought dramatic improvements in energy productivity, but that oil price increase occurred worldwide. For one country, or one region, to impose a significant carbon tax seriously debilitating its economic competitiveness and distorting its industry, even if the tax is fiscally neutral, would be dangerous. Even, as has been suggested, if this were done on a European basis. If at all, the approach must be international and that implies that it will not happen quickly.

My conclusions, therefore, from this brief survey of what actions industry has taken to mitigate global warming as are follows:

–   Industry is taking the issue seriously and has already taken very substantial action with encouraging results.

–   There is much that could still be done in energy conservation which would reduce CO_2 emissions. Industry has a good track record, but needs to step up its efforts.

–   There is advantage in pursuing more efficient generation of energy. Industry is well placed to do this and, in particular, to consider effective combined heat and power generation schemes.

–   The contribution from CFCs will be eliminated and their replacements will have very little greenhouse effect. However, it will be important to continuing reviewing alternatives for their energy efficiency in use, as well as their own greenhouse potential.

–   Industry can make little contribution to reducing methane emissions as a greenhouse gas and, similarly, it does not have a large role in reduction of nitrous oxides, except in one or two specific application.

–   Industry is an effective vehicle for substantial change and improvement, provided that market forces and government legislation give clear signals of what is required in the future.

–   Governments will need to consider carefully how their actions can encourage industry, to act in the right way without undue interference in the market process.

I am confident, in fact, that with the right answers to these issues, industry will continue to play a major role in reducing the global warming threat.

QUESTIONS

(1) QUESTION: Patrick McCully
                   The Ecologist

This is a question for Mr Hampson. He mentioned the non-fluorocarbon alternative refrigerants and said that these were not as energy efficient. It did not look as if they were going to be any where near as energy efficient as the HFC and HCFC alternatives. I wonder if Mr Hampson could tell me how much research ICI has done into non-fluor carbon alternatives?

ANSWER: Christopher Hampson

We have not done a lot of research into non-fluoro carbon alternatives. I think the refrigeration industry has done quite a lot of work in looking at alternatives. I think they are the ones that are best placed to look at alternatives. My understanding is that that work, to date at least, has shown that they are not as energy efficient as the fluorocarbons. That is not to say that maybe, at some point in the future, that may change.

(2) COMMENT: Horst Wiesebach

There is one point which we have not touched upon at all during the whole meeting and that is the trade policy implications. GATT is now starting to get worried about the question of free trade or moving further in the Uruguay round and further rounds and the issue of the environment because environmental standards could very well be used as a non-tariff barrier.

We are, therefore, opening into a completely new policy field and it has already had some effects in the debate on agricultural trade because some governments argue that free trade will be damaging to the agriculture from the environment point of view. This is becoming a very important issue at present, and there is already a big case right now between the USA and Mexico where the USA have stopped importing tuna from Mexico because of the fishing methods used in Mexico which are hurting dolphins and so the Americans said they are not importing tuna from Mexico any more as it has been caught wrongly. Mexico, of course disputes this. This opens up a whole new set of problems.

(3) QUESTION: Kevin Anderson
                  Manchester University

My first question is to David Jones. Bearing in mind libel action can attract in the order of £1 million, do you really think that the sum of £1 million for polluting the Mersey was a large fine to a multi-national company and, if so, why did a similar instance, albeit on a smaller scale, occur very soon afterwards?

My second point is just a comment aimed at Christopher Hampson. I recently spent four years working in the UK's second largest industry, which is the oil industry, working offshore. In that industry, I am unaware that the CFCs are collected from

the oil platforms and most of the refrigeration plants there call for between 50 and 100 tonnes and they are regularly released into the atmosphere.

ANSWER: Christopher Hampson

If I could just add one bit to that. I think that for most big companies what they are really seeking to do is to establish their credentials with the public and the very act of being fined is probably the biggest disadvantage. So whether the amount of fine, a £5 million or £5,000 fine would have made any difference I do not really know. I suspect that it would have the same impact on Shell. It certainly would on us.

As far as the CFCs are concerned, we have set up a system that we will take all CFCs back and recycle them and we have tried to do that with all large industrial users. We cannot force people to do that of course, so all we can do is provide the service and encourage people to do it. I would say there is a lot more CFCs being recycled from large industrial users, than there are from individual refrigerators and that was the point I was trying to make. The difficulty is in collecting it from the small users.

(4) QUESTION: Caroline May
                  Solicitor, Clifford Chance

I work in my firm's commercial litigation department and I really wanted to just make a comment on what Mr Jones had said which builds on I think the comments of the first speaker this afternoon. I act for industrial clients and at the moment what we are seeing is relatively a small amount of criminal prosecutions of clients who, by and large, are very aware, have been very keen to work in green areas at the moment. They have been working very closely with the National Rivers Authority and with their Environmental Health Departments of their Local Councils. These people that they had previously seen as friends and advisors have now suddenly started issuing criminal prosecutions which, by and large, are taking place in the magistrates Court.

One of the difficulties of strict liability offenses is that relatively good operators are being penalised and it is eroding trust, most definitely in these early stages. Industry will think twice I think at local level before going to its Local Council for advise and involvement. On one hand, there is the fear of bad publicity, there is the fear of a fine and a criminal prosecution and, on the other hand, there is the concern about being seen to be green. I think it is an area that we may have some difficulties with. Quite clearly, the law should be applied and I think in the environmental policy for the very worst cases attracting the worst fines, and for persistent or reckless polluters.

My concern is for those of my clients who are trying to comply and take on board the new legislation. Effectively, they are being penalised from day one and it is having an extremely detrimental effect so far on the response of industry to the new legislation. I think it is something that Mr Jones had picked up. I wondered if perhaps was Mr Hampson or any other delegate from a big industrial company could bear out that experience?

ANSWER: David Jones

I have a lot of sympathy with that view. I think these are the sort of things that industry may get very concerned about. The construction industry has been dealt with for some time, under Section 60 of the Control of Pollution Act 1974 in terms of noise on construction sites, and in the early days it took it all by surprise because again it was the start of being prosecuted and there is always civil liability to follow, but affects adjoining owners.

I think they would become really very difficult if somebody suddenly moved the ground rules and we went into this guilty until proven innocent and I do think so much of what the delegate is saying is right because in creating the law, you do want to get some

rapport going with those whom you want to comply with it. Frankly, the best law is the law complied with which we do not spend days, weeks, months or whatever in court enforcing it.

ANSWER: Christopher Hampson

I think that when new government legislation here and integrated pollution control are actually fully implemented, Britain will have the most comprehensive environmental legislation and permit system anywhere in Europe. The amount of information that is going to be in the public domain and required to obtain a permit is one of the concerns that industry has.

As I understand it, the purpose of that legislation is largely to force companies and industry to seek permits for what they are doing and, in that way, control pollution rather than imposing fines. I do not actually think that, at the end of the day, the improvements that everybody is looking for are going to come about through prosecutions and fines. They are going to come about much more by the permit, by the publication of information and by having things on the public record.

One of the difficulties I think HMIP faces is that, in the past, it has appeared that there has been too cosy a relationship between HMIP and industry. I think that HMIP is now going in the opposite direction. I think they have over-corrected, but perhaps that is a phase that they have to go through to achieve the right balance. I do not think we should look at it all in terms of prosecutions. That is really not the purpose, as I understand it, of the legislation. It is to get the permit system going so that companies clearly know what they have to do and have a permit to operate. That is a much bigger threat than a fine.